Wil

Bermuda and North Carolina
1663 - 1796

Based on Research of
John and Sally Cox

1996 - 2004

Edited by Lobo Blanco

© Copyright 2004 Lobo Blanco.
Library of Congress Card Number 97-90349

Note for Librarians: a cataloguing record for this book that includes Dewey Decimal Classification and US Library of Congress numbers is available from the Library and Archives of Canada. The complete cataloguing record can be obtained from their online database at:

www.collectionscanada.ca/amicus/index-e.html

ISBN 1-4120-3217-2

Printed in Victoria, BC, Canada

WILD ROVERS, Settling America.
Bermuda, The Caribbean Pirates and North Carolina
Edited by: **LOBO BLANCO**

Popular History of North Carolina, Bermuda, the Coxes, and of five children of John Cox of Charles Town along the Cape Fear, New, and Neuse Rivers; and of Rich Lands and the American Revolution. Journals, Letters and Conversations.

TRAFFORD

Offices in Canada, USA, Ireland, UK and Spain
This book was published *on-demand* in cooperation with Trafford Publishing. On-demand publishing is a unique process and service of making a book available for retail sale to the public taking advantage of on-demand manufacturing and Internet marketing. On-demand publishing includes promotions, retail sales, manufacturing, order fulfilment, accounting and collecting royalties on behalf of the author.

Book sales for North America and international:
Trafford Publishing, 6E–2333 Government St.,
Victoria, BC v8t 4p4 CANADA
phone 250 383 6864 (toll-free 1 888 232 4444)
fax 250 383 6804; email to orders@trafford.com

Book sales in Europe:
Trafford Publishing (UK) Ltd., Enterprise House, Wistaston Road Business Centre,
Wistaston Road, Crewe, Cheshire cw2 7rp UNITED KINGDOM
phone 01270 251 396 (local rate 0845 230 9601)
facsimile 01270 254 983; orders.uk@trafford.com

Order online at:
www.trafford.com/robots/04-1044.html

10 9 8 7 6 5 4 3 2

INTRODUCTION

I am John Monta Cox, born in 1923 and still living in the year 2002. It is my job to narrate the action in this personal history and to present it as a series of reflections on the part of a line of John Coxes from the 17th century to the twenty first.

The events incurred and the characters presented are mostly true, a few names being added or changed to protect the innocent. The stories are based on several years of research which my wife and I performed throughout the eastern United States, in court houses, all types of libraries, state houses, old bookstores, and in many kitchens and living rooms. Sally, my wife, has performed a great deal of genealogy work and built many family trees on her personal computer. I have looked into the stories behind the court and census records.

I have included many reference citations, journal entries and letters as points of departures for my story line and as starting points for those who may wish to perform their own historical or genealogy research. Or researchers may contact my wife, Sally, for genealogical printouts.

DEDICATION

To the memory of the first
John Cox (of Canterbury)
The Captain of a ketch on Bermuda
in 1663

Whose children and grandchildren sailed ships with
and against pirates and the Spanish

Whose descendents Pioneered and Acquired land in
Onslow County and along the Cape Fear River

To William Cox
Who Migrated to Florida in 1824

To John Hardy Cox
Who was born in 1850 and traded stories with

John Monta Cox, born 1923,
in the 1930's and 40's
born in Michigan, and in 1983 moved to Texas.

POPULAR HISTORICAL NOVELS
by Lobo Blanco

AIR ADVENTURES FROM WORLD WAR II

The Pilot - Jonny Sagan Spends an Exciting and a Happy Time with Girlfriends at Every Flight Training Field in South East America.

Cairo to India - Sean Murphy and the feisty Yvonne Casteel, Flying the C-46 Cargo Plane, Chase a Russian Spy to the Orient.

WORLD WAR II'S AIR WAR FROM ITALY

Endgame - Young American Pilots Flying P-38 Interceptor Fighters Knock the German Luftwaffe Out of the Sky of Southern Europe.

Balkan Thunder - American Pilots Gain Combat Experience in Spain and then Lead the Americans in Battle Against the Germans and the Russians.

A Dangerous Sky - Two British Pilots Fight off the Germans in Greece and then Join the Americans and the OSS Behind the Enemy's Lines.

*EXCITING SEA STORIES OF EARLY AMERI-
CAN HISTORY*

*Sea Rover - Will Palmer, an English Sea Hawk, Res-
cues, in 1605, His Son from North American Indians, then Battles the Spanish and Pirates.*

*Sea Hawks and Pirates - A Description of the Many
Sea Battles of the English Sea Hawks and++ Pirates
and Privateers World Wide.*

*Jo Ellen - This Heroic English Girl in Her Teens
Joins the Pirates, Becomes a Leader Aboard Fighting Ships and Takes Vessels as Prizes.*

PATHFINDERS AND PIONEERS

*Reflections on Life in the Deep South - The Journal
and Letters of Sallie Shackleford Cox during and
before the War of Northern Aggression.*

*New Virginians - Kathryn Humphrey and Gwen-
dolyn Escape from the Indians in Virginia and Battle
off Pirates.*

**Wild Rovers - The Journal Entries and Letters
of the Five Sons of John Cox of Bermuda As
They Become Pirates, Indian Fighters and
North Carolina Revolutionaries.**

BOOK ONE - BERMUDA & THE BAHAMAS

ONE

JONNY LEARNS THE USE OF WEAPONS

My first childhood memories have to do with walking along the River Thames water front, my mother, dressed in a long-checkered skirt and a brightly--embroidered white blouse, at my side. It is raining, soft but steady and my mother's head is uncovered, her hair tousled. We are damp through and through. We hurry and finally arrive at the **Thames Bear Cub** pub, along the quay in eastern London Town.

My mother calls to me, "Come inside with me Jonny. Get out of the rain for a bit before going on to the ship yards."

Conditions were nasty in London Town at this time, in the early 1600's. The nobility and the priests ran things in England and in English possessions such as Ireland and Scotland. It was rob from the poor and enrich the already wealthy.

Some of the lucky families got sent to Ireland

where they were able to be land or property managers and live a better life. But mostly it was a tough life for us. My three brothers and I lived on a day by day basis, often begging food and stealing from street merchants along the London streets.

We Cox brothers, all born in a village near Canterbury, near the mouth of the River Thames, had little to look forward to except to go to sea or to war.

My mother worked at the **Bear Cub** while my brothers and I worked part time at several ship yards, the Eastern Market, or for captains who were tyrants over those loading and unloading their vessels as well as on board their ships at sea. The word of a captain was law and they had the power of life or death over seamen aboard their vessels. It was a trade off; war, or the life of a slave.

In about 1645, during wars between England and France, I was pressed into service with English Sea Hawks, privateers and pirates. I was twelve at this time, being born in 1633. Very quickly I learned the techniques required in order to stay alive and to outlive the domineering captains and mates under whom I served.

Being light and an apt athlete I spent many hours in the rigging climbing and setting the sails on the ships as all oceangoing vessels were driven to their destinations by use of the wind. It seemed that minor corrections were constantly needed in order to optimize wind use. When we got into fights with other ships I became a member of a gunners crew, loading, unloading, aiming and firing a cannon.

I was given a cutlass when I first was taken on

board and made to learn how to defend myself and to fight and kill enemies. After getting cut up in an incident with pirates who were trying to board and take our vessel an Arabian mariner took me under his wing.

Asa-ed-din said, "Hey you young buck, you nearly took one through the throat there."

"I slipped."

"You don't handle the weapon properly."

"Oh? What should I do?"

"First, hold the sword out in front of you with one hand."

"It's heavy."

"Trade for a lighter one."

"Then what?"

"Train your muscles so you can hold and turn the cutlass with one hand."

"What of the other?"

"You can place a scimitar in it."

"We call them Warwick Tooth Picks where I come from."

"Where is that?"

"I'm from Canterbury, where the finest story teller since Homer who told about the Greek Wars of long ago, resided."

"Who was that pray tell?"

"My uncle, one Geoffrey Chaucer, who wrote the book, **Canterbury Tales**. It's all about the different kinds of adventures a series of travelers who stop in the Canterbury Inn have had along the roadside."

"I've heard the name but not read any of the tales."

I then asked, "Scimitar?"

He said, "It has blades on all four sides."

"Oh? I've never seen these kind of weapons.

"How is it used?"

"You keep it in your less-used hand and use it mainly to help you balance your body while swinging around with the big blade of the cutlass or sword in your stronger hand. When your opponent and you both have swords extended out ready to cut in to lay the weapon with the sharp blade turned toward you; you ward off the opponents blade with the scimitar while yet bringing in your cutlass alongside your opponents side. If he wards off the sword with his arm, you cut the arm off, keeping the sword in a full momentum swing into his torso."

"And the scimitar?"

"You hold the opponents weapon and then twist it between two of the scimitar's blades, forcing his weapon out of his hands. Then thrust the scimitar into your opponent's ribs while giving the weapon a strong turn to the right."

"What does that do?"

"It cuts up his insides and renders him useless to his side; he falls to the deck and spills his blood and guts all about. Other sailors and pirates slide and fall on the deck. They become easy prey."

And so it was that I began a program to build my muscles and to secure several quality weapons.

After five years before the mast as an able bodied seaman and apprenticed navigator I became a seasoned mariner and gunner. Because of my navigational skills, I was sought after by the captains of merchant ships, privateers (vessels for hire to one or another nation or local governor), pirate crews and by the British navy. Through it all Asa-ed-din remained by my side and helped me through many battles.

One day in 1650 we joined in a mutiny against a French privateer captain after our water crew took him and the first mate captive off the western coast of Italy at Ginova. We all met in the captain's quarters and discussed what to do as mutineers..

Germany Schultz said, "We could burn the vessel, sell the cargo and blend in with the town's people."

I said, "I don't like that idea."

Scott said, "Lets go adventuring and capture a few other vessels, split the loot and then go ashore and discontinue pirating."

Asa-ed-din, our Arabian Turk, said, "Let's elect a captain and get the hell away from Porto Fino. We can talk about what to do once we clear our tails and have some free time."

And so we became a free vessel available for hire or for taking prizes.

Once we were out to sea, Asa and I talked about the free ship.

I said to him, "Asa, now we're all stuck with this ship and all eligible to be hung by the nearest country's ships."

"We could take several ships with cargo and retire early with enough money to last each of us for several years if we're lucky."

I said, "We'll just fight ourselves over what ever we capture."

Asa said, "It seems as though our ship was doing

rather well."

I responded, "Yes but those who live as pirates and free-booters live an uncertain life."

Ada said, "Our vessel carries twelve guns."

I said, "The privateer-owner has sailed us onto the Tyrannean Sea just off western Italy."

Asa called for the crew to vote for a captain. He said, "We want somebody smart, who knows how to manage a ships sails and her guns. Jonny is sort of smart. I vote for him."

Scott, "I don't care who the captain is as long as its not Schultz."

We voted ourselves members of the Brethren of the American Coast. If we were caught now, we could be hung without any further trial.

We had an election and the brethren elected me, just seventeen, captain. I found myself the leader of a band of cutthroat buccaneers with no specific loyalty to any country. Our vessel and crew were then available to the highest bidder as a privateer. We renamed our ship the *Sweet Candy*.

When we could get no one to sponsor us with lettres-of-marque we operated under the black flag of the pirate. I was sailing the robber's wind; one which would lead me to the end of a rope strung to a yardarm aboard some sea-venturing ship.

In 1655 the English under Cromwell were in desperate need of support naval forces for a major attack on the Spanish at Jamaica. I sought lettres-of--marque from the Cromwellian government and to join forces with the English in the Caribbean. Here were the British general, Robert Venables and the admiral, William Penn.

Although these commanders were incompetent, our rag-tag forces were nontheless able to gain victory. Jamaica became British and an haven for those pirate and privateer crews who had helped the British. Pirates held dominance over many smaller islands in the Caribbean and among the Sommers Islands.

One of the pirate captains who had fought with me in the Battle for Jamaica in 1655, a Captain Barranau, had a small fleet of ships in his flotilla. He had appointed himself Governor of the Sommers Islands, including the Bahamas and Bermuda. Governor Spotswood of Virginia later wrote of him as being a hard-nosed and evil pirate.

In 1660 he invited me and my vessel to join him at Nassau. So I brought our ship, the **Sweet Candy**, into Nassau determined to become an adventurer as were my family ahead of me.

TWO

A PIRATES' SANCTUARY

Nassau wasn't much of a harbor. It had no facilities. We came into the bay with the intention of finding a harbor master to direct us to a destination where we could drop anchor. There was none. Asa-ed-din, my mate, and I tried to make out some sort of pattern to how the ships were placed but without success.

Finally we just found an open spot which seemed close to shore, dropped the **Sweet Candy's** anchor and a small boat. I had the small boat take Asa and me into the beach. We walked from the beach into the town and found a place for us to eat. Then I went to look for Barranau, my French friend while Asa cased the rest of the town with its tented cottages (tents used as roofs) and grog shops.

Barranau had taken over one of the grog shops and had an office above it. I climbed the staircase keeping a hand on the handle of my sword.

"Governor Barranau, Captain Cox and the **Sweet**

Candy reporting for assignment," I said.

"We've no formality here Jonny boy. Sit down. Have a cigar," Barranau opened a box setting on his desk. He handed the box to me. "Straight from Havana."

"Thanks, I will." I took one, then another.

Governor Barranau asked, "You have anything pressing you have to get done?"

"Get my crew fed and get the barnacles off the **Sweet Candy's** hull."

"Do you know anybody in this part of the world?"

"I have a couple of kin on Bermuda Island I think."

Captain Barranau said, "Those islands along with those here in the Bahamas were included in a charter granted by the King in 1615. It went to the Governor and Society of ye City of London for the planting of one or more plantations (or colonies) of the Summer (Somers) Islands and granting divers libertyes (liberty or freedom) to them and their successors."

"So the islands belongs to England?"

"I assume so."

"But you control it?"

"Not really, but we watch out for it. We're part of the Pirate Community."

"So my kin over there are English citizens?"

"Perhaps."

"Makes for a lot of nonsense."

"So maybe you should go and try to make some sense of it."

Bermuda

So Governor Barranau had his administrator prepare some papers for us. We were assigned to repre-
sent his (Barranau's) Barony on Bermuda.

The governor said, "The English have two forts
on the island but have them only lightly fortified or
garrisoned.

"I expect the British to send a lot more marines to
build up the fort. In the meantime you can take command of the islands if the British leave or the Spanish take over.

"Jonny, don't start fighting with the British
though. I don't fancy fighting with Cromwell or any
other official government military unit."

"Can I get some property?"

"Absolutely. Stop and make arrangements with
the commander at Southampton Fort. Then you and
your crew can plan on living there for awhile, until I
am disposed of here anyway."

"Are there rules or laws?" I asked.

"Lots. But you just worry about an invasion by
the French or Spanish. Send word if things look
bad."

When word got around that the **Sweet Candy** was
headed for Bermuda, several rough-looking buccaneers made their way to our little boat waiting on the
beach. We added several to our numbers and headed
out.

One who called himself Cotton Eyed Joe had
been working this part of the world for the previous

ten years. He and I had a discussion about the make up of the community.

Cotton Eyed Joe's Story

I asked, "What do you know about these islands?"

Cotton Eyed Joe started off, "The Bahamas have been an unprofitable possession of the English since 1609. In many instances there was no English governor as it was not a location where a governor could gain any riches.

"Its main use is by privateers and pirates who use it as a place for their own harbors and ports. They prey on the Spanish vessels returning to Europe with plunder from their wars with the Indian civilizations of Mexico and South America.

"The pirates also capture vessels in the Caribbean Sea and Florida Straits carrying slaves from Africa, the fine wines of Europe, and gold from South America.

"The commercial ships use the Florida Straits located between the Bahamas and Florida and the Gulf Stream paralleling the southeastern North American coast to hurry their way home. The rogue Sea Rovers sail to the middle of the Gulf Stream and wait for their prey to come to them from out of the southwest. When the time is ripe they drop their Spanish or English banners and fly the black flag of the pirate. When they attack they seldom show their prey mercy.

"Pirates are greatly feared as many are notorious for their ability to inflict torture. Others are kind and gentle; yet others are weird in their approach to command and battle.

"Many of the pirates are men who had not been able to earn a living in the normal course of events. Being a pirate, inflicting outrageous damage and injury on normal persons, enables us to raise our ego for a brief period.

"The pirates at Nassau not only use the town for relaxation from living the robber's and killer's life but also enables some of us to start a new life as a shop owner, a shipwright, or a banker. Some own grog shops or pubs which draw patrons in on a recurring basis.

"And a man can pick up a woman here without having to worry about marriage. Those few women at Nassau who are married have had their husbands go off to sea often never to return. The pirate's life was not one with much longevity.

"From time to time, the rulers of one or another nation declares an amnesty for pirates. Maybe there would be a war on and the ruler needed more warriors or ships. The pirate then had merely to renounce piracy and to swear allegiance to the ruler.

"These occur often during a ten year period. But sometimes the ruler or his agent will not fulfill their obligation and we pirates are taken captive or killed.

"Whatever, it is a dangerous life."

THREE

SOUTHAMPTON FORT

So we sailed out to Bermuda and put down stakes at Southampton Harbor just off the Little Sound on the south west corner of the islands complex.

During our three day sail from the Bahamas, Asa-ed-din said to me, "Jonny, this accumulation of pirates in one area where they can be safe from the big Spanish and French merchants ships and the naval ships guarding them can't last."

"Oh, I asked, "Why not?"

Asa said, "Some of the colonists and the governors representing some of the nations object to pirates having it so easy as Barranau has it. They're going to send big flotillas of gun boats to police the Caribbean and along the North American and the Central American coasts."

"We'll just have to wait and see."

After a series of complaints from the Governor of Virginia about the pirates operating along the

American coast, England sent a ship to the Bahamas under the command of Commodore George Rogers with the intent of taking firm control of the islands and wiping out piracy.

In the summer of 1663, the commodore, working out of Nassau, offered pirates an amnesty if we would swear allegiance to England.

Barranau sent word to us, "I have signed on for the amnesty and recommend that you all do so too."

Asa and I discussed the potential with young Lieutenant William Seymour, the son of Commander Florentius Seymour, the commander at Fort Southampton on Bermuda.

Lieutenant Seymour said, "I don't see any harm in you seeking amnesty. You're pretty loyal to the English most of the time anyway."

"But we don't want to become part of a fleet that chases our friends who decide not to seek the amnesty."

"Try it and see if you can just give up piracy and not get into the anti-piracy business."

In 1663, I sailed into the bay at Southampton Fort, renounced piracy, and received a pardon. My pardon was signed by Commander Florentius Seymour. In spite of my objections he put me and my crew to work chasing pirates and keeping the Spanish at bay.

My crew and I, now under a Letter-of-Marque, captured and took as prizes two more ships. We use them as part of our own fleet of merchant vessels, operating a courier and trading service between the islands, Charles Town and Philadelphia.

I have now sailed some of the worse seas in the

world, an area called the Bermuda Triangle. Here the weather is wild and the flow of the water is unreal, like a back current running north and east, and extending deep down into the canyons of the ocean floor.

But I am now a respected Merchant Captain and adventurer. As a ship captain, I get to move in pretty good company. Along the way I fell in with Lieutenant William Seymour, then serving at Southampton Fort, on Bermuda Island. His grandfather was captain of troops at the fort. The lieutenant and I supported one another on several occasions during bar room brawls.

Ed Cox's Story as Told to Sam Cox

Uncle Sam Cox told me about our earlier ancestor adventurers who were residents here on Bermuda.

Sam started off, "Ed Cox was an able-bodied seaman on the *Sea Adventure* in 1609. He told me his story."

Ed said, "While on a sea journey to replenish supplies for the colonists at Jamestown, the ship, on which I was an able bodied seaman, the *Sea Adventure*, ran into a hurricane and we were driven onto the rocks of an unknown island in the middle of the western Atlantic Ocean. The *Sea Adventure*, flying the flag of Sir George Somers, beached herself on what is now called Bermuda. We managed to get ashore and to careen our vessel on the sand beaches on the leeward side of the island. It was 23 July 1609.

"The island is located some five hundred sixty

eight miles due east of Cape Hatteras, North Carolina.

"And it's not an island at all, but an archipelago of over a hundred islands making up a complex of some twenty square miles standing on a mountain top in a deep part of the ocean. The water within the islands, and around it, are clear and made up of exquisite hues. There are fair skies, sunshine and flowers all year long. The climate is equable and untouched by fog or frost. The residents are free of tropical fevers."

I said, "That's quite an island history."

Sam said, "That's not all. Ed continued on,"

Ed said, "We lived out the summer here and named the place Virginiola. But by now Admiral Somers, our captain, had died of injuries incurred during the hurricane, so we renamed the islands the **Somers Islands** in his honor. The weather was such a delight that I decided that I would love to live here always.

"By spring we managed to build two small ships from the wood of the *Sea Adventure*. We called them the *Patience* and the *Deliverance*.

"In April 1610 we mounted the two small ships and again headed west toward the coast of North America. In May of 1610 we entered the mouth of the a river, the *James* and immediately saw the colony's ship exiting the river.

"The colonists had just about run out of provisions. But now they reversed direction and all three ships returned to James Town where we delivered our supplies less what we had used to get through the winter on Bermuda.

"I was surprised to find an absence of women but

it was so because this first venture was really one of scouting out the potential for building a colony in the New World. From now on ships would carry persons who were more prone to migrate as full time colonists of Virginia.

"By 1611 there were 700 English inhabitants of Virginia, 30 of them women. At this time the colony was building town houses, the first floor being brick and the second built from the available hard wood from the deep forest."

Sam said, "I asked Ed, "So how did you end up here in 1616?"

Ed told me, "I went back to England on one of the bigger vessels in 1610 and told the family what I had experienced.

"There was not much support for Virginia by the Crown so in 1611 several of the leading adventurers, including Richard Cox, switched from venturing in Virginia to venturing in Bermuda. Here the climate is more appealing and the mosquitoes nonexistent.

"In 1615 the London Company received a separate document for the Somers Islands Company. This company was to include the islands know as the Bahamas as well as Bermuda."

Richard Cox, 1616

Sam Cox continued Ed's story, "In 1616, Richard Cox and I came back on the *Sea Venture II*. I put down stakes here as a planter while Rich continued on, representing the family as an adventurer. I became the agent for our family's business in Bermuda and Rich took the *Sea Venture II* and delivered our produce including our fish to the colonial towns along the American coast from Jamestown and further north.

"So I was able to start a family, build a house and earn a living without traveling to sea very often."

Sam Cox, 1625

"How about your story?" I (Jonny) asked

Sam answered, "My family was part of the sea going community in Canterbury of course. When I was a boy, our extended family owned several ships which we used to do trading with the Dutch, the French and the Belgians, just across the channel from us.

"Richard Cox, my pa, had me working at the family shipyard, building one or two ships a year for use on the Great English Channel, the wildest body of water in the world.

"And I have the good fortune to live right next to its entrance from the north.

"I was but twelve years old now, old enough where my pa pays me a might for what I do in the yards. So here I am just off work with my pockets clanging with coins. Being young and debonair I walked the quay in London Town.

"My father caught up to me on this bright moon filled night"

My father said, "Sam, it's time you went to sea and learned a bit about the business of merchandising the products of southeastern England."

"Must I? Life is too sweet here in England. The weather changes nicely and you and mother are good to me."

"You have to start doing a man's job."

"The family requires that we have men that we can trust managing our ships and our stations. Right now we have a need for a man to sail with and soon manage our vessels between here and our business in the colonies."

"I'm only twelve."

"You will grow older," he said.

"So you came to Bermuda?"

"Hard life, eh?"

"That was in 1625?"

"Yes, as a factor on a ship that missed the islands and got lost such that we were at sea for three months and ended up back there at London Town with no cargo delivered."

"That must have gone over well with your father."

"Yes. He fired my ship captain and made me the captain, turned the ship about and soon sent us off again for Bermuda with instructions to not come back without getting rid of our cargo and without another from that side of the world."

"How did you, at only twelve, control the crew?"

"First, I'm big for my age and next I had been given a tremendously big and strong mate named Big Ox. My original trip over the Atlantic and back, where we got lost was a great experience for me. I learned to navigate on the ocean. Now with my own ship and with Big Ox as my mate things went great for us.

"As soon as we passed out west of our British Islands I proceeded to place the *Sea Venture III* on the latitude corresponding to that of Bermuda and stuck to it come high winds, rain, storms, snow and deep troughs in the wave patterns.

"Wambo! We came directly on the islands from the east. I never again had any trouble navigating. I just never trusted my location from a longitude standpoint."

"You have any trouble once you arrived here?"

"Well Uncle Edward insisted that I trade our goods from England right there in Bermuda and then that I mount a trip to the mainland. By then the weather was turning colder and hurricanes were in the making.

"But off me and my ship went and we pulled into Philadelphia just before Christmas, made our trades and reloaded up such that we beat the coldest weather and arrived back at Bermuda before the end of January. And the weather was still nice in Bermuda. I could understand why Edward Cox wanted to live here for ever."

"Anything else?"

"I had some wrongs done to me by Captain Nathaniel Butler, Governor of the Somers Islands. I had several vessels under my command by 1631, just puddle jumpers, going back and forth to the mainland. He wanted to charge me taxes as though I was a big merchant ship.

"And then later in 1631 my community appointed me to be its Reader for the Smythes Tribe. This meant that I was similar to being a mayor or priest. Believe me, after being your own man for several years, being subject to a couple of hundred people with different wants is much more difficult."

"They call you the Capes-Merchant?"

"Yes, now it will be your turn to carry that title and to sail our ships to the mainland and to merchandise our product."

[Ed. Roger Cox was a member of the Grant Inquest for Northampton Tribe in June 1652.

Sam Cox died in 1655...left items to widow Martha, April 1655.]

FOUR

THE ONION PATCH

John Cox Interview by brother Joseph

"Jonny, you seem to have lived on this beautiful island forever."

Jonny answered, "Yes. And as a ship captain, I get to move in pretty good company. Along the way I fell in with Lieutenant William Seymour, then serving at Southampton Fort.

"We supported one another on several occasions during bar room brawls.

"Eventually, on September 12, 1655, Lieutenant Seymour had me over to his home for dinner"

"Good?"

"That's not the point. I met Billy's sister, Joan Seymour."

"My sister-in-law."

"The two of us hit it off from our first meeting. We seemed to have a similar concept about life and marriage. She was a strong-willed girl as well as being very pretty. Within a month we agreed that we intended to marry and within three months we actually married."

And what did the Seymour family think about this?

"Not much."

Billy Seymour asked, "Jonny, how you going to keep her happy? Feed her? You've nearly no education except for how to sail a ship and fight with a cutlass."

"We'll work it out."

Billy said, "Baa..a. Marrying for love doesn't put bread on the table."

I loved her

Jonny and I, his brother Joseph, continued our talk. I asked, "You seemed to fall in love very fast."

"From the first time I saw her I thought that she was a very pretty girl. She wore no make up yet her face was glowing, maybe because it was so recently washed."

"A washed face?"

"I don't know that. But she had great eyes, dark brown like my own. And she had neat hair, not at all long, but a deep-dark red with a bluish-green kerchief tied round it setting it all off. She had a relaxed style of dress, a green blouse over a long sweeping skirt which flowed round and about. I could see us floating about a dance floor with that skirt weaving in and out among the other couples."

"But you only square dance."

"No. You haven't been with me for several years.

I've been to some Spanish communities and learned to dance to a different drummer than what you learned in jolly old England."

I asked, "This was all before you talked with her?"

John said,"Yes. Then I heard her talk at the dinner table; it was like hearing the robins sing and the mocking bird respond to to other birds, sweet, loud enough to be heard, yet not overpowering in strength of sound. Each word was clear and I understood her sentences with clarity. Further her utterances all made sense; the sentences fit together in logical thoughts.

"I found that right away I could enter my thoughts into those which she uttered. We communicated at once and in depth. She was busy with some matter foreign to what we were doing, eating a meal; she was solving another person's problem; and she was doing it with supreme logic."

I said, "Your love seems to be one of the mind."

Jonny laughed, "Ha!"

I questioned, "It's more than that?"

"In the evening everyone went to a play but Joan and I were left alone."

"So?"

"She invited me to see her room on the third floor. And I followed her up the staircase to the room. She opened the door, went in, and left the door open inviting me in too."

I asked, "Was it a nice room?"

Jonny smiled, "She sat on the side of the bed and began undoing the buttons on her blouse. And then she lay back."

She asked me, "Do you like my bare shoulders?"

"What did you do?"

"I moved over and sat beside her and slipped the straps off her shoulders. I kissed the nicely tanned shoulders and continued to help her undress. Before long she was sitting there completely naked, the nipples on her breasts protruding forward."

"And you?"

"I starred at her body. I had never seen anything like it. She had the most beautiful body I could ever imagine. It was lily white and when I touched a nipple the nipple turned orange. When I kissed a nipple she leaned her body toward me and I nearly died."

I asked, "You were fully dressed?"

Jonny said, "Hell no| My body yearned for hers and I too was quickly in the nude.

"We thrashed about for awhile and my private part showed what I had to offer her."

"You offered, and her brother came home?"

"I wanted this girl like I had never wanted any girl ever in my whole life."

"Well, did you progress through the whole way?"

"No. I held her close and we hugged one another, but then I dressed myself."

"Why was that?"

"I didn't want her spoiled for me or for someone else if we didn't marry."

"Sir Goody himself?"

Again she asked, "Do you like my shoulders?"

"They are the most beautiful shoulders in the world," I said.

Joan said, "Do you like my breasts?"

"There can be no others that compare. I love all of you and especially the you that is inside of all this beauty."

Captain Florentius Seymour

I asked Jonny, "In 1655 the senior William Seymour died and Florentius took his place as Commander at Southampton Fort. How did you get along with your father-in-law?"

Jonny continued, "Pretty much all right, Joe.

"It bothered him that his daughter had married a pirate captain with almost no education. But what could he expect in our wild land where there were nearly no educated people. But Joan and I really love one another.

"Further, as soon as Joan and I had a child, we named him Florentius after Joan's father.

"Florentius is now Lieutenant Governor. In addition to being Lieutenant Governor he continues to hold his title of Captain. He captains the military unit on Bermuda as well as being Commodore over several English naval and privateer vessels. Some of these were captured by and were captained by part--time pirates."

"Do you have any other information about him?"

Personal information:

    1615 - Captain Florentius Seymour born.
      Married Ruth, daughter of Stephen Paynter
      Fathered; William, Jehoidden, Elizabeth and
        Joan Seymour.
      1655 - Florentius was appointed Captain
        (Commander) of Southampton Fort.

I asked, "What of your property?"

Jonny said, "I was a resident of the Devonshire Tribe (or Parish) in 1663 at which time Richard Norwood conducted a survey identifying my property as being coded as no. 11, consisting of 49 acres per the survey.

"More recently, on August 23, 1673, I have been elected to be a member of "ye council of ye Assembly of the Somer Islands".

I asked, "What all have you done to earn a living since you got here in 1655?"

"Well, I've had my ship and a couple of others with less carrying capacity so I have worked with Sam at managing a small shipping business between here, the Bahamas and the mainland, about eight hundred miles on a leg. I raise crops on my fifty acres of land; and then I do a little pirating when the time is ripe. Of course I do a lot of loving with that woman I described to you earlier."

"I hear that you have a ship called the *Exchange Ketch*. What's a ketch?"

"A ketch is a fore-and-aft rigged ship similar to a yawl but with a larger mizzen and with the mizzenmast stepped farther forward."

I changed the direction of our talk, "Jonny, we were both born and raised in southeast England, near Canterbury and the extended mouth of the River Thames down from London."

Jonny answered, "That's a big sentence, but yes, I agree. It was from here that many of the ships bound for the new world started. Many of our young men took up mariner careers, becoming sea captains, crew members or pirates."

I said, "You and I were scheduled to join the family business, adventuring and sailing on English Channel and across the vast Atlantic Ocean. We joined our uncles and cousins in the family business in Canterbury while still in our teens, taking on mariner tasks and representing the family as a factor on land and a sailor on board the big ships."

Jonny interrupted, "The name Cox appears in the Parish books of Canterbury, England for the 15th and early 16th centuries. Many of the other surnames in the Parish of Canterbury are identical with those of the early settlers of the Somers or Bermuda Islands. The whole group of islands here are called the Somers Islands."

I added, "The Bermuda Company was chartered by 'James by the Grace of God, King of England, France, and Irelande, Defender of the Faith.' It was assigned to the Governor Companie of the Citie of London for the Plantation of the Somer(s) Islands, June 29, in the 13th year of King James.

"You got spirited away one day and eventually ended up here as a pirate captain with a pirate crew.

"Now you've married Joan Seymour, the scion of a sea military and merchandising family. Joan is the daughter of Florentius Seymour, appointed in 1655, Commander of the Southampton Fort.

"I (Joseph) rose to be a captain with the Cox family of merchants and adventurers, and I ultimately moved, with my family, to the Cox station here on the Somers Islands only to find you here before me.

"I'm hoping that we can work together on sailing

our ships and manning our trading station here, on the Bahamas and eventually in Charleston."

Jonny said, "I'm for that Joe. Maybe I can settle down to the extent that one can in this new world, what with wars with Spain, France and the Wild Indians, not to mention the buccaneers and pirates."

I responded, "What can be greater than living on a mountain top in the middle of the ocean, with a warm climate all year long, no mosquitoes, and an ocean view in all directions?"

Jonny responded, "Nothing that I can think of."

FIVE

OUT JOAN'S BACK WINDOW

Journal Entry by Florentius Cox

My father, John Cox, was killed in a Spanish raid on Bermuda in the winter of 1677. The will was written in 1671 and probated on March 12, 1677. As usual my father, John, was right in the middle of a fire fight with ships blasting their cannons at one another with mighty broadsides.

I, Florentius, sailed as second mate as our sloop of war left Devonshire. My description of the weather and fight is as follows:

"The night was pitch black; the moon and stars were blotted out by a sky clothed in a thick layer of stratocumulus clouds and there were no stars visible.

[A war sloop is rigged like the smaller sports sloop built for speed with but a single-mast. It is fore-and--aft rigged with a short standing bowsprit and a single headsail set from the forestry. It is larger than a gunboat but carries guns on one deck only.]

"We sailed the *H.M.S. Opportunity* out of the sound and immediately headed east, driving our way along one leg of the Bermuda Triangle to directly cross the Gulf Stream to Charles Town. There we would change direction and head north to pick up the stream's current and rendezvous with our sister ship, the *Adventure* at the mouth of Cape Fear River.

"The wind sang in the rigging and changed tune often as the *Opportunity* twisted and turned on the waves causing father to balance with the roll. We all watched the bowsprit reach for the sky, complete the roll to the starboard then slowly slip down the wave on the port side. She had performed a corkscrew roll and made ready for the next thunderous wave.

"I stood on the deck and allowed my mind to wander with thoughts of home back in Bermuda and of the girls I would take walking along the sounds as the full moon set over the endless ocean rolling waves to the west.

"I talked to my father who came by the wheel as I held the sloop on course."

Father said, "I have been considering about what will become of you, my son. You are already becoming a mariner and warrior."

I thought on the subject but said nothing.

Father smiled as he watched me at the wheel struggling to keep our vessel going in the right direction toward the vast continent to the west.

Father continued, "I think of our little ship in the center of the Bermuda Triangle, filled with vast waves constantly on the go, churning, always churning, and twisting our ship from a nearly vertical position going up a huge wave to diving down into a trough.

"And is it here where we expect to find a Spanish ship filled with plunder from the Inca Indians of Peru."

"How old are you father?"

"I think I was born in 1630, so I'd be about 47 now. Your Uncle Joseph is about three years older.

"Remember son, I have written a will and it's in my brother's care, with you as one of the executors. So if anything happens to me, go to old Joseph and he'll bring forth the right papers for distribution of my assets."

John's Will actually goes as follows: "I leave my wife, Joan (Seymour) Cox, two land shares on Bermuda at Devonshire (49-50 acres), from the sea to the onion patch. My oldest son, Florentius Cox (b. c1660), is left my other land, my vessels and the big work table. My personal estate is to be split between Joan and the rest of the children.

"My brother Joseph is to be the Overseer of the will; Joan and Florentius are to be the Executors."

Journal Entry - Joan Cox

"I am the daughter of Governor of the Bahamas and Somers Islands, Florentius Seymour. I had married John Cox, (b.1630), then a resident of Devonshire, and the Master of his own ketch. I received John's estate in 1678/9. It was valued at L335.18.10 including a large bible and 8 servants.

"Some consider me headstrong because I had resisted my family's desires and had married John Cox, a roving privateer and sometimes pirate-ship master. But our marriage has lasted until now and we have been extremely happy except when John is off on one of his ventures.

"Those who own ships and master them are generally both pirate and privateer depending on what suited the occasion."

My Youth - Joan Seymour Cox

"I was born in 1635 and can not remember anything about my birth. My mother, Ruth Paynter, tells stories of my childhood, including my insistence that I be allowed to go to parties at age three when I was still too young to be quiet and genteel. I apparently disrupted things with my shouting and my temper.

"But," Mother Paynter says, "you finally got over that stage and became rather genteel. But you have always loved parties and dressing up. That may be, in part, because we live in such desolate conditions and so far away from proper civilization. Then too your family has always been among the leaders in the community."

"I was the youngest child in our family, both Jed and Liza being older, seven years for William, five years for Jed and two for Liza.

"We have always lived in quarters furnished by the British Army, as father has been a commissioned officer serving at stations away from England, usually on duty under his father, William Seymour.

"My great-grand aunt, Ann Seymour, was Queen

of England, one of Henry VIII's wives, but nothing came of that. But Ann was reputed to have been a beautiful woman at the court. I used to think of myself as her reproduction, as my skin has always been lily white. John used to dote on my body, saying that there was no lovelier thing on the face of the earth.

"But I have never used any paint on my face, priding myself on having a clean, well scrubbed, face. John loved that too.

"Mainly I pride myself on my mind though. I can outthink nearly every man that I know of. One of the reasons that John and I were attracted to one another was the fact that we could think together, solve problems. We thought a little differently, yet reached similar answers about the problems of life.

"There were no schools on Bermuda, except that every so often a teacher might stop by and receive permission to hold classes for a month or two. It then became the duty of my mother to select a location for a class room and for contacting families who might be interested in sending their children to a learning session. Thus over a ten year period I attended classes for about fifteen months. I learned to read rather well since I could read independent of school and so move ahead fast. We also studied a little arithmetic, English grammar, Latin and sewing related subjects.

"Early on I was attracted to boys. I found that I could tease them and get them all excited by placing my body close to them such that they were aroused. Then I would leave that boy and go tease another.

"When I was sixteen I met John. At my first opportunity I got him to hug and kiss me. Then when we two were left alone for what I thought would be an hour, I coaxed him into my upstairs room. There I nearly drove him wild showing off my pretty body. He undressed and was was fondling my nipples when I heard the front door opening in the front room. My parents had returned early|

"John set a record for getting dressed and removing himself out my back window to the ground fifteen feet below.

"Father called from the stairway. 'Joan, Joan, are you up there?'"

"Yes father, just cleaning up a bit."

Father asked, "Is John up there?"

"No father, I believe he's out back."

"In the months that followed I teased John often and he came to me like a kitten. But we soon thought of marriage and John wanted me pure, so we didn't do anything that could spoil our marriage. But we did decide then that we wanted to marry very soon..

"John and I were promised to one another within a month after meeting and were married while I was still sixteen."

SIX

ESCAPE from the BLACK BART

John Florentius Cox tells of his father's life on Bermuda and aboard ships

My father, Florentius Cox, was born on Bermuda in about 1661 and was named Florentius, after his mother's father. He spent the first eighteen years of his life there being jointly raised by his parents and his uncle Joseph Cox, also a resident of the island.

Living on the waterfront he quickly learned to manage small boats with sails, sailing on the inland waterways of the island and also off shore all about the island.

Bermuda is an island that is often the object of the wrath of major Atlantic Ocean storms, including hurricanes.

Florentius was one of a half dozen youths and young women apprenticed to his Uncle Joseph, learning to work around ships, becoming a shipwright or a mariner (sailor).

Flor (his nick name) and others, including Polly and Nick, managed to build two small sloops which they used to sail about in the sounds of Bermuda and to race clear around the big island.

"Was Polly a relative?"

"No, but she and Flor were close friends, eventually marrying and becoming my parents."

In one race around the islands, the apprentice sailors were caught by a strong storm and thrown to the mercy of the heavy winds and seas. The second crew was unable to get its sails under wraps soon enough so that the sloop was cast about in the seas and driven west. With nearly no control the little vessel was eventually cast upon a rugged pile of rock with no other land visible in any direction.

Flor, Nick and Polly had battened down their vessel until the storm passed.

Flor said, "The storm seems to be about over now. Shall we return home or hunt for our buddies?"

Polly said, "Let's try to find them. Maybe they made it through the storm alive but with a vessel with no controls or sails."

Flor said, "Nick, you agree?"

Nick said, "I'd want someone to look for us if we were the ones in trouble."

And so Flor, Nick and Polly sailed in the lee of the storm after the first sloop, thinking to find and help the first crew if it needed help.

Two hours along after the heavy storm the second sloop was sighted. The crew indeed needed help. The vessel was atop a rugged rock pile. The sloop was being pounded by the surf and the sea waves.

Flor said, "I'll be careful not to get close to the rocks."

Jacoby, on the second sloop, called over, "You just stay down wind from us and we'll cast you a line. If we can't get a line to you we'll let it float along."

Flor and the second sloop stood by the rockpile casting lines back and forth to the wrecked sloop. Finally things were calm enough that the two ships got themselves strung together enough that Flor could take a ship's boat in the water to the wrecked sloop.

Concentrating on the wreck, Flor, Nick, and Polly did not notice the presence of a third much larger vessel until the rescue was nearly completed. By then the third vessel was set to board and take the good sloop. The new vessel had a deck that was clear of rubble and set for fighting. It flew a black flag adorned by a white printed set of crossed bones. It carried about a crew of thirty pirates.

Flor and his five fellow apprenticed sailors and shipwrights were not prepared to fight, not carrying weapons and were worn out from effecting a rescue.

Bartolomew Portugues and his crew of cutthroat pirates took Flor and his friends prisoner without a fight and confiscated their sloop and limited cargo of food for lunch purposes.

The six captives were thrown into the brig and the pirate ship, the *Black Bart*, took up a headeding for the Bahamas and a planned gathering of a big group of pirates there.

Bartolomew was known to be a cruel and savage pirate who dealt harshly with his prisoners. Accordingly the six apprentices were anxious to find a way to escape, perhaps by using the sloop which was being dragged along behind the **Black Bart**.

That night one of the pirates secretly slipped Florentius a long sharp knife. "Maybe this will help."

"Thanks, you come with us ?"

"No, I like this life. I'm just sorry for you and the girl. Maybe we'll meet again under different circumstances."

In the night's darkness Flor slipped from his bonds and moved to the deck. There he moved to the shadows of the masts and stored booty on deck. He came up on one deck hand at a time and slit three throats before any pirate could let out a sound.

Returning to the hold where his frends were incarcerated Flor whispered, "Here, I'm cutting you each loose. It's about four in the morning. Nick, you and Polly go noiselessly and gather in the sloop tied to the stern.

"Jacoby, you cut the rope between the vessels and we'll be off into the starlit night."

When Florentius climbed aboard, Polly had already got a bearing on the stars. "Keep the North Star to the right Flor. We'll head straight for Virginia."

Under Polly's direction the sloop was headed directly to the west. The six man crew hoped to reach the mainland before being caught by the larger pirate ship, the *Black Bart.*

After sailing for another two nights the little crew and the sloop sailed into a bay by a little fish town on the on Shackleford's Banks, just east of the North Carolina sea coast.

John Shackleford, the sea captain, turned ship builder, careened the Cox sloop, and soon had the vessel repaired. The six apprenticed sea persons were soon supplied with food and water and headed back to Bermuda.

Florentius managed to withstand the rugged weather of the Bermuda Triangle within which he regularly sailed; and eventually he replaced his father and uncle as the captain of a ketch carrying supplies between Bermuda, the Bahamas and the mainland towns of Charleston, Philadelphia and New York.

Florentius Cox, when he was twenty years old, married Polly Ann Rush, his youthful companion on this sea adventure. She was the daughter of Isaac Rush of Charleston, South Carolina. They had three sons, including one named John.

Florentius Cox lived on Bermuda raising his family and then helping raise five of his son John's children after John was wounded in action against the Spanish.

Florentius Cox's Will

This will was probated in 1736, although it was first signed in 1731. Florentius Cox Sr. left houses and lands off the islands of Bermuda and New Providence to his three sons, Florentius Jr., Thomas, and John. He provided otherwise for his daughters,

Martha, Ann and Sarah. The children were born between 1685 and 1695.

Son Florentius Cox Jr. was sent to New Charles Town to be educated. He later helped manage the family ship-building business, becoming a journeyman shipwright and manager of ship-building operations.

Florentius was elected to the House of Assembly and expelled with two other members in 1738 for misrepresenting in London the action of the House. In 1740 he was elected Speaker of the House.

Second son, Thomas, remained in Devonshire on Bermuda, becoming a planter and managing the family's operations. He married Mary and had a will dated in 1761, listing children Susannah, Jane, Rebecca, Martha, Florentius, James, and John.

SEVEN

REHABILITATION in CHARLESTON

John (Florentius) Cox, third son born to Florentius Cox and wife Polly Ann (Rush) Cox, was born in c (approximately) 1682. He was the second male in lineage to bear the name John Cox and he was honor bound to bring credit to the name. As it happened he had an opportunity to fight against England's enemies, both the French and the Spanish.

Children

John began having children in the early 1700's, beginning with Issac who took over management of business affairs and then five other boys in sequence, each a carbon copy of their father and grandfather. They loved the sea and what that signifies; sailing, battling the elements and living in towns close to the sea where they could trade with mariners and with mainland planters and traders.

Battling the Spanish and French

1703/06 - In October 1703 and again in 1706 the combined fleet of the Spanish and the French sacked and plundered Nassau. The six Lord Proprietors had not provided adequate protection for the local citizens.

John (Florentius) Cox (b. c1682), Florentius Cox's son, commanded a war sloop, a large vessel on which he could mount twelve cannons. In addition to taking cargo back and forth to the Bahamas and to the mainland, John Cox had lettres-de-marque given him by the British commander in Jamestown so that he could, when appropriate, take to the seas as a British privateer.

John Cox said, "Besides me, there were perhaps a dozen other mariners with their own vessels on Bermuda. While these vessels were too small to take on French or Spanish man-o-war vessels with their big guns and on-board marines, they could provide the British with information about the enemy and engage if they could do so in consort with several other privateers.

"I named my ship the **Wild Rover**. With it properly staffed I, and other resident privateers, attempted to defend the Somers Islands including Bermuda and the major town of the Bahamas, Nassau. The distance between Bermuda and Nassau being so great, and the ships available to myself and the Bermuda Islanders being so small, the defense was not very great."

"Once in 1714," John said, "I was told of a French ship anchored in the sound at Bermuda. My neighbors and I attacked the foreign ship on a night absent the moon, coming in close and mounting the French ship's deck quietly, locking many of the French marines below deck.

"We took some cargo and a few weapons, then let the ship and its crew go.

"In 1715 - In the absence of help from England and from the Lord Proprietors, pirates from the Caribbean decided to move their headquarters to Nassau.

"There were too many pirates for us to fight. We just gave them the town. In return they permitted us to come to Nassau to play and to trade."

Battling who? Likely the Spanish.

In 1715 the pirates at Nassau found the pickings pretty good as the Spanish had to send their treasure ships along between the Bahamas and the mainland along the Florida Straits. The Spanish were having difficulty with both England and France and were in need of the treasure to help finance their build up of marine power. Already the English had taken several islands from them, including Jamaica. Now the English also had a strong land presence in America, primarily the English colonies along the coast of North America.

Just now the English and the pirates had taken

common cause.

The English, which had a claim to the Bahamas, was recruiting privateers from along the coast and in Bermuda. Times were not good for the Bermudans as shipping lanes to North America were closed by both the Spanish and by pirates. So the opportunity to earn some extra change as a privateer captain was looked on with favor.

John said, "While captaining a privateer defending a Pirate attack on Nassau, I fought in a big hand to hand battle on the decks of my own ship.

"My main adversary, a huge pirate sporting a black beard and a flowing red bandana, shot me in the head and drove a dagger into my chest just where my heart was supposed to be. I'd been tripped from behind and lay helpless on the bloody deck."

The first mate, Jacoby, said, "John was left for dead, but the heart of this fighting mariner could not be stopped."

But John had to give up the rugged life of a mariner, privateer and sometimes pirate. John left his sons on Bermuda with their grandfather, Florentius, where they could live an outdoor life in and near the sea.

John said, "I, my wife and daughters, and my oldest boy, Isaac, moved to Charles Town, South Carolina where I lived a life of partial retirement."

John Cox's Journal Entry re. Charleston

"As soon as I was able to move about and get out of the King Richard Hospital in Charleston, I bought a cottage type home on Church Street. Soon after, I had a home built to my specifications, with a half dozen bedrooms and a court yard, near the water front. I proceeded to work as a shipping merchant.

"I bought and sold merchandise from the mainland to merchants traveling to New York and Philadelphia and to the East, mostly to Canterbury, England."

Joseph, the business oriented son, wrote in his journal about his father, "My father was not satisfied with the sedentary life and, besides, he required exercise to keep healthy. So he took to the woods, much in supply in the region close to Charleston and the Cape Fear River. He and my four young brothers, when not in school or staying with Grandfather Florentius or sailing, spent time hunting, fishing, hiking or canoeing. As a sideline they and I searched for open land which might be patented.

"Martha, my mother was a slim, dark-haired woman, filled with energy. She found a job with the city eventually becoming an assistant to the city manager, monitoring city administration and devising better ways to manage operations. She became an icon at city hall as she raced about on a horse drawn cart carrying out city business."

Florentius

[Ed. So Florentius Cox, (John's father) at age 60, found himself acting once more as the father of a brood of boys until his own death in 1731.]

Joseph found himself appointed executor of John's will which was written and signed before 1738, and was probated on January 19, 1744.

Joseph says, "The will calls my father a mariner, which of course he had been. It tells what was to happen to the house in Charleston, S.C. where the proceeds should be used to educate we five younger boys, unnamed, until the youngest one (me) was educated; also what was to happen in the event that Grandma Martha married after he died.

Martha did marry so that, in accordance with the will, the oldest son, Isaac inherited the big house in Charleston after educating the younger five boys."

EIGHT

FIVE BOYS AND THE SEA

A Conversation: Florentius and Polly

I, Florentius, paced the verandah of my villa in Devonshire on Bermuda. Polly Ann sat on the porch, using one foot to push the swing back and forth. She watched as I, her husband, blew off steam. "Polly," I said, "I'm at my wits' end. God knows, I've tried to raise these boys right. But I just can't keep the young whelps in check!"

Polly Ann, my pretty wife, now dressed in white blouse and a black and white checked skirt, shook her head. "They're just like their father. I fear for them. They're becoming pirates for sure!"

"Living here on Bermuda, the five youngsters have a carefree life; fishing, swimming, sunbathing, and beach combing.'

Polly said, "Perhaps they should spend more time with their father in Charleston."

"Look, here they come now, up from the boat yard. They walk in a column, John, Moses, Joseph, Anthony and Charles.

"As with their pirate father they are leaning toward lives at sea. They'll suffer his problems too, probably, being wounded or killed by the Spanish or by pirates. before they reach twenty five."

"They are so young yet," Polly said. "They range in ages from six to fourteen years."

Florentius Cox had retired from the mariner's life in 1700, and, until the British left, had lived the life of a prominent colonial landholder on Bermuda. His mother's father, Captain Florentius Seymour, had been Lieutenant Governor and Governor of the Somers Islands, including the Bahamas and Bermuda in the period after 1680. Florentius' father, Captain John Cox, had been a member of the Council of the Islands. Captain John Cox's behind-the—scenes activities had been a major factor in Captain Florentius Seymour's being appointed Lt. Governor.

As with so many in public or political favor at the time, Florentius Cox's assets grew exponentially during the years his family had held colonial offices. He had acquired considerable land on the islands as well as adding to the land of his paternal grandmother in the Carolinas. He received many grants in return for political influence peddling with the Lords Proprietors. Six of the eight who were Lords Proprietors of the Carolinas held similar positions in the Bahamas. And they were no more actively involved in one than the other.

Polly remarked, "The boys have all the material

possessions that they could ever want."

Florentius responded, "Yet they are drifting away
from us. The two older boys spend spend too much
of their time on the sloop I gave them from some
long forgotten venture I had. Now they sail across to
Nassau on New Providence Island and find their fun
with the pirates and privateers there.

"Polly, the boys, just children yet, have taken to
drinking, to womanizing and to fighting. They're
husky lads, but little do they realize that the pirates
hanging out at Nassau on New Providence Island
would as soon run you through as not."

"What can you do about it?"

"I don't know. They won't listen to me. They call
me an old sea dog that doesn't know the new tricks
of the business. Boy, that has a familiar ring to it.

"Grandpa, they say, you've been a buccaneer. Why
shouldn't we?"

Polly said, "Buccaneering is all right. But the boys
may end up going against the law and become pirates."

I said, "Perhaps they'll end strung up on a yardarm."

Polly said, "Flor, think of your forebears. Some of
them were Horsemen and Vikings who plundered
the coasts of Europe."

"I thought of them as "needing" to venture out a--
viking so as to acquire plunder to be traded for food
so they could feed their families."

"Ha, probably they just went a-viking for the sake
of the adventure. This viking spirit still runs, as an
inherited   factor,   through   you   and   your
descendants."

"Do you think it will continue forever till finally

one day the young men will all be hung?"

I said, "I was a heller myself as a young man in Nassau. That town was a miserable place to live. Men were getting killed on the streets and down the lanes without reason."

Polly said, "It was like this for my father too. He lived a tough life but one with which he certainly was fully satisfied."

NINE

CAPTAIN HORNIGOLD

The tent city of Nassau on New Providence Island was a haven for pirates. Here four of the more adventurous boys, Charles, John, Anthony and Moses were able to listen as the mariners exchanged tales of their adventures in the Caribbean and along the coast of North and South America. The buccaneers, whether pirate, sailor or beachcomber, shared a hatred for Spain.

To the boys it seemed that these men lived the most exciting of lives. They were the "Black Knights" of the Caribbean. Many of the heroes among the pirates used New Providence Island as their home base, especially since Port Royal, Jamaica was no longer open to them as it had been in the past. One young pirate, a Thomas Barranau, was a descendant of an earlier Barranau who was the leader of a pack of pirates located on the Bahamas. He was the self proclaimed Governor of the Somers Islands.

Charles talked with Governor Barranau, "What

kind of work can we get to stay out of trouble here at Nassau?"

Barranau said, "The only steady work is that of being a crew member on board a privateer or pirate vessel."

Charles continued his questions, "How about working for an eatery?"

"You could wash dishes or clean the floors."

Charles said, "Captain Hornigold is advertising for crewmen."

Tom Barranau answered, "Yes. He could teach you things about the sea. But you might become a pirate that way."

Note: The Bahamas are located in an area of the Atlantic Ocean that is particularly treacherous due to the currents, hidden shoals and adverse weather conditions. The pirates generally had vessels that were smaller than the merchant ships, sloops and brigs, which could carry only a few big guns. But the pirate and privateer ships were fast and maneuverable.

Barranau continued, "Nassau is a place of temporary residence for a floating population. Ship captains came to the island in hopes of recruiting a few mariners and buccaneers to add to their sparse crews. Sailors, especially tough men, willing to fight and use the cutlass, are in much demand now. The pay is good and often the crew gets to share in the prizes taken."

On the one stone wall left from the wars, Charles took notice of an announcement: "Captain Benjamin Hornigold, master of the *Cougar*, a brig with twelve guns, requires mariners looking for adventure and wealth, to sail the south seas, to help our country against the Spanish and French. Must have seagoing experience, be strong and be able to handle a cutlass and other weapons. Especially need gunners."

Soon the *Cougar* sailed from the bay at Nassau sporting Lettres de Marque signed by Tom Barranau, Governor of the Bahamas. On board were two sailors, Charles and Moses, hoping to become wealthy mariners.

Big-Ben Hornigold was the acknowledged leader of the buccaneers at this time and a feared captain. His destination was the Spanish Main, the sea lanes where Spain marshaled its cargoes of gold and silver. Here it put together convoys of huge merchant vessels, the galleons, for their treks from South and Central America along the Gulf Stream to Spain.

Periodically Spain organized an armada of its vessels at Havana. From here the ships sailed up the Florida Straits following the Gulf Stream and the prevailing winds along the American coast, then out to the open sea, across the ocean, to Europe.

Charles addressed a letter to his brother John:

Dear Brother John,

"Finding not a ship under sail across the whole of the Caribbean, Captain Hornigold had us turn north. We now follow the Gulf Stream along the Florida coast and past Georgia, and the Carolinas. We stop small merchant ships from time to time, threaten them with our big guns and plunder their cargo. We're obviously pirating. Both Moses and I are concerned about this.

"At Beaufort Inlet, Captain Hornigold careened our vessel to clean the barnacles. I rowed Captain Hornigold to the small village, called Diamond City, to talk with the shipwright there, Mr. Shackleford.

Captain Hornigold said, "l would like to have my vessel inspected for defects and get some reoair work done."

John Shackleford said, "The Shackleford Boat Works can do most anything. It looks as though you could use a new forward mast and some new planking on your deck."

Charles volunteered, "Our yards need work too."

.

For two weeks the crew of the *Cougar* sported about the beaches and visited the shanty town on the mainland where liquor and women were to be had.

Charles added in his letter, "I know that I'm complaining because Hornigold is pirating but in truth he has been a good teacher for both Moses and me. He's also a difficult task master. He and his new Lieutenant, Ed Teach, drive the crew hard and have taught Moses and me much about handling the brig's two masts and the numerous types of sails.

"Write me in care of General Delivery, Nassau."

Charles Cox, able bodied seaman

The Cox brothers plan to go to sea.

After a season of privateering and pirating with Captain Hornigold and a second with Captain Charles Vane, Charles Cox and his brothers, Moses, Anthony and John, even though all were less than eighteen, felt ready to captain their own sloop.

Charles offered, "Boys we have to rig our ship to fight."

Moses said, "Get me some cannons and one of the family sloops and we'll start putting a war ship together."

John said, "I'll get the sloop from home, the bigger one I suppose."

Charles said, "Right, and I will start recruiting a crew of young men in their late teens and early twenties."

"From where?"

"Why from Bermuda, from along the Carolina coast, and from New Providence Island. Many of the recruits will come from among those with whom we've sailed on earlier ventures, but now we'll be the captains and we'll have our own cannons."

Charles, with John, Anthony, and Moses as Lieutenants, set out for the Caribbean Sea in the spring of 1717, joining forces, first with two of the Shackle-fords from Gloucester County, Virginia, and later with Ed Teach, the one called Blackbeard. With the Shacklefords, they sailed as English privateers; but with Blackbeard every vessel was a target. They flew the black flag with skull and crossed bones. Joseph became the boys' agent, selling their share of the goods taken from the vessels taken from pirating or privateer ventures.

Goods were sold in the towns northward along the North American coast.

By 1720 the four Cox boys had become seasoned mariners, privateers and pirates, who lived quietly with their grandfather on Bermuda. Occasionally they vacationed at home with their father in Charleston. They had to keep their presence secret when in Charleston as even part-time pirates, were held in low regard by the authorities in the towns and on the islands.

Even so, many of the merchants were happy to do business with the boys as their prices were far less than the regular merchant from England, Spain or New England.

They had outlasted Captain Rogers who had been sent by the English to root out the pirates in the Bahamas. They lived well on their take from their sea going adventures and they had learned well the fine art of when to fight and when to run away.

Anthony was asked about the Cox's business. He said, "We own two fast sloops, which are highly maneuverable. Tactics have changed across the years.

"Pirates no longer carry large quantities of cannons; instead they have a larger crew of top fighting men who can mount and defeat crews of sailors. Our men are compensated strictly from our loot and prizes."

John and Charles wore short beards, more sporting than that of Blackbeard. They were now among the most skilled practitioners of those who use the cutlass to enforce the way of the pirate at sea.

TEN

LA CAROLINA

On July 17, 1725, Don Juan de Seville y Cordoba, captained the galleon, *La Carolina*, as it headed for Spain. He lifted a goblet and held it before him in the direction of the party at the neatly decorated table. "To the happy couple. May the good Lord bring them happiness."

Rebecca O'Brien glanced at her duenna by her side, as she rose and acknowledged the toast. She could tell that the others were set on drinking toast after toast. She left the dining and drinking hall and headed for her cabin. Don Bonito de Cordoba bowed her out.

He asked, "Is my cousin unhappy with our betrothal?"

She responded, "It's just that I can't stand talk of nothing but the sea. And the big black cigars from Havana, make me feel ill."

He said, "I'll see you in the morning?"

She said, "Yes of course."

"I hope the ocean is not causing you to feel ill."
"No. I'm sure it's just the cigar smoke."

Rebecca's duenna, one Isabella, helped her prepare
for the night. Rebecca's dark hair had to be brushed
through one hundred times.

As Rebecca sat before the mirror she thought of
her father, Admiral O'Brien, Captain of a Man-O--
War for the Spanish King. Such it was for Irish lads.
They fought against England in the only way they
were able, as hired knights for the armies of France,
Spain and whoever else would hire the Gaelic lads.

Her father had been posted to Havana, to direct
the ships furnishing protection for Spanish vessels
along the Spanish Main lines in the Caribbean as
well as to and from Spain. For three years now, Rebecca had lived in the Caribbean, serving as her father's household manager and companion. Her
blazing red hair and freckles set her apart from the
other women in the Spanish community. But her pe-
tite figure and good cheer made her welcome at all
the parties.

Now they were going home to Spain. Her father
commanded a Man-O-War furnishing protection
for a large armada of commercial and protecting war
vessels.

Isabella asked, "Why are you unhappy, Mia?"
"I am but a stranger in Spanish society. Yet here
I am engaged to a Spanish nobleman. I don't even
believe in the concept of noblemen!"
"But isn't it well for an Irish lass to marry into nobility? Haven't the prettiest girls from Ireland always been the source of wives for noblemen from the

Danes to the Romans, from Scotland to France?"

"Yes. It's true. We're often taken because of our
spirit and our beauty. But we would rather stay in
Ireland with our own Irish lads. I would rather
sweep out the dirt floor of a common Irisher than lie
on the soft cushions of the Spanish King. Marriage
without love is no marriage at all. And a sin against
God you know."

The sea was heavy, the waves were high and the
night was pitch black. The thirty ships moved si-
lently through the night. Rebecca and Isabella went
back up on deck to catch some fresh air, as it was
moist and close below decks.

The Lieutenant on duty saw them. Bowing to Rebecca, he said, "Dona O'Brien, please, no one is allowed on deck in this fearsome weather. The Captain especially wanted me to watch out for your
safety. I am sorry."

"What is it? The ship seems to be bobbing so vio-
lently."

"I think the Captain will come about in a few minutes. Maybe conditions will improve. It's hard to
keep the other vessels in sight in this weather and on
such a night."

Returning to Rebecca's cabin, the women could hear
the sailors moving about the deck, running as com-
mands were called. The motion of the galleon
changed as the sails were rearranged and they took
up a new course.

In the morning, the storm had subsided and the
sea was back to normal. The Captain took up a

heading of north by northeast and followed the Gulf Stream. But they were alone.

The armada had disappeared. Had it gone on without them?

Overhead, the sounds of the sailors could be heard again. The cannons were being rolled out and the sounds of the men heave-hoing on ropes were heard. Now the crew was preparing for a fight.

Don Bonito came to their cabin door. "I'm afraid that we're about to be attacked."

"Attacked? By whom? We're not at war with anyone now. Who would dare attack a Spanish Galleon in an armada?"

"The armada has been broken. We're a ship by itself, the favorite target for the English, French or American pirates. You're to lock your cabin door until after the fight is over."

"Who will win?"

"That's in doubt. The attacking vessels are sloops, two in number and they appear to have no cannon."

"No cannon? Why we should win easily."

"Maybe. Sloops are very fast and maneuverable. Our ship is big and clumsy."

Locking the door, the two women listened to the sounds of the fight.

They heard the sound of the first mate as he screamed to the captain, "Damn them! We can't get lined up to use our cannons for a broadside. They're coming at us from the bow and stern."

Rebecca listened with all her energy. She caught the

words as the Captain urged his men to fight. A
scraping noise was next identified as she picked up
the sound of grinding metal as the pirate grappling
hooks were caught on the galleon's rails.

The pirates from the sloops climbed up the side of
the ship and boarded the galleon. All hell broke
loose on the deck. Within five minutes it was all
over. The women waited and wondered, for they
knew not who had won the battle!

Then the sound of hurrahs filled the air and footsteps came racing down the stairs. It was the pirates
coming to ascertain the value of their prize. One after the other, the women heard the sound of axes as
the pirates smashed in the locked doors below deck.

Finally a cutlass smashed through the panels in
the door of Rebecca's cabin. A man sporting a black
patch over his eye and a bloody wound in his left
arm entered the cabin.

"And what have we here? Sure and you're a little
beauty," he said, addressing Isabella. "Come with me
little one.

"As for you, Missie," he said to Rebecca, "The
Captain will want the likes of you."

Taking Isabella by the arm, the pirate forced her out
of the cabin ahead of him, and into another cabin
across the way.

The one-eyed pirate shouted up the stairwell,
"Captain. Captain. Come on down and see what's
waiting for you in cabin eight!"

Rebecca backed into a far corner and watched
wide eyed in terror through the cabin's open door. A

half dozen pirates passed her cabin, stared in at her and moved on to other places searching for valuables, to other rooms, to the hold and to the store room.

And then a burley ruffian stared into the cabin where Rebecca huddled against the wall. "Aye. And what have we here?"

Reaching a big hand, smeared with blood and dirt, up to Rebecca's shoulder, he ripped her soft pink blouse half off, revealing her pure tanned skin and a single alabaster breast. The pirate had the scent of sex and wasn't to be deterred. Grabbing the young girl by an arm, he shoved her toward the bed, stooping to begin removing his baggy pantaloons as Rebecca came up hard against the wall. Getting one leg free he started on the other.

At that moment, the youthful captain stood at the door. He looked in and sized up the situation quickly. "Ah Low, the captain said, "Having a little fun, I see."

"She's mine, Cap. I found her first."

"Sounds good to me, Low. You giving up your right to a share of the cargo?"

"No, I ain't," the pirate, Low, said. He looked at his captain inquisitively.

Rebecca, sensing the boy at the door was indeed the captain, cried out, "Captain! Captain!. Save me from this brute! You dirty, slimy pirates will all hang for this. My father will see to that!"

Captain Charles Cox grinned at the pretty young girl, "You're no Spanish maiden! That's for sure!"

Rebecca took up a lamp and went after the pirate, Low. "Damn you! Damn you!"

"And you're no lady either I hear! Stop it," the captain said. With one hand he retrieved the lamp and with the other he sent Rebecca flying across the floor of the cabin, drawing blood from a split lip. "I can't have vicious prisoners injuring my crew men!"

Rebecca was furious. She began to weep. She huddled in a corner. The more she cried the madder she became. She was so furious that her whole body shook. Low stared at the girl in the corner. He reached down to remove the second pants leg.

"Now, Low. Keep your pants on, man. Then get the hell out of here. I'm claiming this one as Captain's privilege."

Low, a picture of frustration, held himself at the ready, wanting the girl with all his desires, yet unwilling to challenge the captain. He slowly drew the first pantaloon back on, constantly keeping an eye on the half exposed white beauty with the long red hair. The blood dripping from her face made her even more desirable. He hesitated as the pantaloon reached his knee.

"Want a little action from the captain?", the pirate captain asked. He drew his cutlass. "Come, I accept your challenge right here and now."

The pirate captain's cutlass dripped blood from personal combat on *La Carolina's* deck. He'd beheaded three of Don Juan's men and severed the left arm of the captain before *La Carolina* had struck her colors.

Low completed dressing himself, leaving the cabin and the girl to the captain.

The captain followed behind as Low left the

cabin, then reached over and locked the door. He looked at the wild-eyed redheaded girl. "Can I trust you to make no further attempt to escape?"

"Rebecca cried out, "Can I trust you to set this vessel free and to release me?"

"Ah, my beauty, you've no an idea of what the situation is I see. No you may not. You are a prisoner, a newly elected slave, with no rights at all. And you belong to me. The moment I release you, a dozen of my men will line up to rape you, one after the other. You may die in the process."

"You're just trying to frighten me."

"I hope that I've succeeded for I can not waste any more time explaining the gravity of your situation for you and for of your servants."

"Oh my! Please protect my Isabella."

"And where, pray tell, is this Isabella?"

"Across the way in another cabin where a second pirate took her."

"I'll look into the situation. You just stay here and stop screaming or I will have to have you gagged and tied to your bedpost. Do you understand?"

"Yes captain."

By noon the situation between *La Carolina* and the two sloops was completed and *La Carolina* was under the command of one of the young mariners from one of the sloops. Many of the crew members not yet killed or seriously wounded, had been allowed to join the crews of the pirates, as British sailors, for the sloops flew the British Ensign.

La Carolina thrashed her way westward under reefed sails, a northeasterly wind laying her onto her portside. Rebecca was allowed on deck where she could talk with the temporary captain, a young man named John Cox who had received a wound on the forehead in the battle just completed. His bandage kept coming loose until finally Rebecca took it on herself to see to the wound and to redo the bandage in a better stage of repair.

The wind sang in the rigging and blustered about Rebecca's ears. Had it not been for the earlier happenings on board the ship she would have felt that all was right with the world.

She thought of the captain and his control.

She asked, "Captain John Cox you are very young to be a captain of a ship. How old are you? "

"I'm twenty two ma'am. Not so young as you might have supposed. Besides I have pull. My brother is the senior captain of our little flotilla. He's only twenty four. My third brother, Tony is eighteen and he is captain of our second sloop. "

"And your older brother's name is what?"

"That would be Charles. We call him Captain Charlie. Named after the king, you know, the one what lost his head."

"I don't know much about English history."

"And I don't know much about Spanish vessels, especially big ones like this. Please excuse me while I try to keep our ship in line with the two sloops. "

Rebecca watched as Captain John stood on the quarterdeck of the three-layered Spanish commercial vessel, heavily loaded with an unknown cargo. As yet the pirates, or English privateers, had not determined the value of their prize. They would be pleasantly surprised when they found that it contained a cargo brought from Peru, up the Pacific to Panama, across the landbridge to the Caribbean, and reloaded onto this vessel. Peruvian cargo often consisted of gold; Inca gold from the mines of one of the two oldest civilizations in the Western Hemisphere.

John felt good about capturing a Spanish vessel, especially one which traded in merchandise from Peru, for he felt that he was in some way continuing the fight of the Incas against the conquistadors of Spain. That fight had started in the mid-1500's and was continuing still, a hundred and fifty years later.

There was no let up in the weather; John balanced against the roll of the galleon, as the massive waves passed under the ship from the stern. The stern rose high leaving the bow pointed down into the space behind the previous wave. *La Carolina* slipped to the starboard down the back of the wave as the bowsprit followed behind the stern digging its way out of the trough and then twisting as the next wave picked up the stern again repeating the cycle.

Each wave seemed to pick up the merchant ship and to heave it forward into the air before dropping it back into the trough. The vessel heeled a little down current, in the direction being taken by the waves. The pitch and roll was rhythmic and John was soon balancing on the quarterdeck, as though dancing a waltz. He could have been happy in the refreshing wind if not for the fact that he had to be always on the alert for the approaching coast of North America. Many's the ship that had been lost here in the Bermuda Triangle, known for its odd current from the Florida Straits and for the mysterious disappearances of many ships on their way from the Caribbean to the North American coast or to Europe.

Today the little flotilla was lucky and John

sighted land to the west in time to notify his sister ships and to change courses to the north, toward Charleston and home.

At this time, all the prisoners [other than Rebecca] from *La Carolina* were transferred to the sloop captained by John. He sailed south to an area of the continent known to be occupied by the Spanish, then found an isolated coastal area of the content, where he dropped off many of his captives. Quickly he left the captives and began sailing north to catch up with his brothers at Cape Lookout and Core Sound.

Instead of entering the harbor at Charleston, the three vessels sailed to Core Sound and Cape Look Out Bay. The North Carolina government had been good working partners with the pirates back when England was at war with the Spanish or French.

Some of the Shackleford family adventurers who had migrated to North Carolina in the early 1700's owned land off the sound and operated businesses at Fish Town and Crystal City on the off shore island. These were small villages on the Shackleford Banks and on the mainland, adjacent to North River.

Leaving the large Spanish vessel at sea with one of the sloops, the other sailed into the Beaufort Inlet and into the Bay. The bay was empty of other ocean-going vessels.

John Shackleford and his two sons, James and John Jr. welcomed the Cox captains and provided them with anchorage in the bay and on the sound.

It was here where the cargo from *La Carolina* was unloaded and evaluated. The bay was located in the big arm of a cape extending ten miles out into the Atlantic Ocean and itinerant vessels often stopped

stopped here so there was not much interest in the three privateer ships.

As goods were unloaded, they were either hidden on the Shackleford Banks, placed aboard one or the sloops, or sold for ten cents on the dollar to Shackleford Shipwright Ltd and the Palmer House Trading Post. These later goods were stored in the Shackleford warehouses on the property at the point where the North River meets the sea. John Shackleford used the goods to trade with his neighbors, with Indians, or with merchants from or in other cities or colonies along the Atlantic or in the Caribbean Sea..

By now Rebecca had been able to observe Charles in action. He had let her alone for much of the trip so far and she had in her own mind decided that he was the fellow that she could actually love and would chose to marry. Yet she held back.

In Charleston she was living with Charles' family in the large three story house that Father John owned on Market Street.

ELEVEN

ADMIRAL O'BRIEN

The story goes that Vice-Admiral O'Brien learned of
the loss of the galleon with his daughter aboard
while he was still at sea. Within a fortnight he arranged to be switched to a sloop and headed back to
the Americas. But because of the currents and wind,
it was six weeks before he arrived at Havana and ini-
tiated a search. Three months had passed by the time
he caught up with Captain Charles Cox. By then Rebecca had fallen hopelessly in love with Charles. But
she was still not tamed. The happy two young persons were living together in the Cox compound in
Charles Town, then an English colony.

One night Admiral O'Brien sailed his slick-fast
Spanish sloop into the bay. With only four marines
he raided the town and found out where Charles was
sleeping. Finding Charles and Rebecca he quickly
determined that a Catholic priest was needed. Not
finding one he settled for an English Church-of--
England monk. He took Charles captive and gave

Rebecca a choice, "Marriage vows with Charles or a necktie party with Charles the one with a rope strung around his neck?"

The admiral watched as the vows were given, He said, "Ah. It's a marriage made in Heaven."

Admiral O'Brien sailed off on his sloop, returning to his duties with the Spanish naval forces. He smiled as he thought of Rebecca and her new found spouse. He said to his first mate, "Happy I am to be back at sea."

"Why is that sir?"

"I've managed to turn over responsibility for my head-strong darling daughter to a big strong English pirate captain."

"That's good?"

"Yes. No one else would be able to tame her."

Charles and Rebecca were none too happy at the forced marriage that they had experienced. Charles looked at Rebecca and saw a spoiled brat of a young woman, used to getting her own way on nearly all affairs. True, she was attractive, beautiful if the truth were known and she sported a soft complexion. He liked it even though her face and arms were covered with freckles, left over from her parents Irish and Scott extraction.

Rebecca looked at Charles and saw a brute of a man, strong and too bright to be connived by such as she. He had a ruddy complexion and sported a tan over that part of his body which was exposed to the sun. At sea he moved about the decks wearing cut off pants and a bandanna tied about his forehead. In town he had a bright deerskinned jacket, purple pantaloons, a shinny white shirt and a big captain's hat.

He looked pretty good but she could not stand being married to him, though a Catholic Priest had sanctified their marriage. How she hated her father and how she hated Charles. She was furious when Charles knocked at her door.

"Go away," she called. "I have no desire to see or hear you."

"I agree. But we must talk and make plans."

She stood inside the closed door, "What plans? I want to go home, back to England, or to Ireland?"

"Well, which is it, girl?"

She opened the door, "You may enter and have a seat. But I don't accept that I'm married to you."

Charles sat down, "That father of yours is nearly as headstrong as you are. He says if we don't stay married he'll come back and have us both tarred and feathered before he burns us at the stake."

"He wouldn't do that to me."

"You can stay here in our compound if you promise to control your temper."

"And if I don't?"

"You can become a prostitute. You can wander the streets to find your customers. And you can contract the illnesses that your sex partners might bring along."

"Oh, I hate you."

"Then you chose prostitution?"

"I didn't say that."

"You'll stay?"

"For the time being."

"You have to pay for your keep."

"How's that?"

"My father says you can keep the stalls cleaned

out and feed the horses."

"I can do that?"

"Yes. And you can teach my two youngest brothers to read, do calculations and to write English."

"That's Anthony and Moses?"

"That's right."

"What of you, Joseph and John?"

"John and I are going to have to switch occupations since life at sea seems to be becoming dangerous. We're going to see if we can't find some land up the Cape Fear or one of the rivers in North Carolina."

"And Joseph?"

"I expect that he'll run the family business from here in Charleston."

1728 - John Palmer, scion of the Palmer family trading business in the lower colonies, was picked to captain an expedition against the resurgence of the Yemassee Indian Nation. They had retreated into upper Florida in about 1720 after some particularly difficult times with the South Carolina backwoods traders. Now they were conducting nuisance raids in concert with the Spanish.

Palmer and his expedition, including the five Cox boys of Charles Town, executed a daring campaign through the woods and over the seas directly to Saint Augustine where the Indians were soundly defeated and nearly whipped out.

For their efforts during the campaign and for earlier efforts against Indians in North Carolina, the militia men were awarded tracts of land of their choosing up the Cape Fear River water shed.

TWELVE

CHARLESTON

Captain John Cox's Journal Entry

When I was wounded and moved to Charleston I found that I had many problems. I had to find a house in which to house my several children and close to a place where they could be educated. And I wanted to be able to live life without much renown as I had enemies who would like nothing more than to be able to find and attack me while I was sore weakened from my wounds.

Martha however needed an active life in the community. Thus Martha and I selected our new home together, having a three story house built on Church Street a block off the waterfront. It was close to several churches and within walking distance of a school taught by Miss Walker, a woman known for her large library. Church Street gave us a choice of religions, most of them Christian. Personally I tend to follow the leanings of that minister up in Massachusetts by name of Emerson. I've been reading some of his essays too. They say he will be down here one day to lecture to our women about being self reliant.

We have five bedrooms, four on the second floor and one on the smaller third floor, along with a play room. I had three outhouses, one for Martha and me, and others for the boys. I found that the many bedrooms soon became necessary as Martha and I soon added to our sons Isaac, Joseph, John and Charles, with Anthony and Moses. We also took on a natural born boy, one who had been born out of wedlock. What happened to his father and what his name was we do not know. But his mother turned young Jacob over to me to keep until he reaches the age of twenty one. He has become a part of our extended family. He works on the plantation and I have had him taught to read and write. I expect to remember him in my will.

The young boys, all born since I retired to Charleston, all attend school for several months a year and will until they choose to quit.

Life in Charleston is pleasant; the weather is mild; and the living is easy. There is plenty of ways for the boys to be busy and to earn money by working for mariners, boat builders, etc. There are many buccaneers about and those who would be pirates. But the boys have seen a couple of pirates hung by the neck here in town so perhaps that will hold them in line.

I try to keep the boys at school or busy at work dur-

ing the cold months and to send them to stay with
my father Florentius in Bermuda in our hot summer
months. My father accepts the boys all right but he
has been complaining of late.

Life is reasonably comfortable as I had socked away
a large sum from my pirate plundering days.

Outside of Charleston, I use an alias name when
living in the back woods, Lobo Blanco. Further, I
dress in garb more suitable to the Indians; a dried
deer skin jacket and trousers. I sometimes adorn my
head with two eagle feathers. On my feet I wear
moccasins.

My boys, when they accompany me into the
woods, often dress as I do. They avoid much contact
with the Indians except when called on as part of the
militia forces from Charleston and the lower Cape
Fear River.

The Indians are usually peaceful. But they sometimes want a show of strength if we meet near one of
their villages. I'm getting a little old as the years go
by and I do have my wound which hasn't yet fully
healed. So I have to rely on trickery if I become engaged in a one-on-one fight with an Indian warrior.

BOOK TWO - NORTH CAROLINA

THIRTEEN

THE YOUNG PIONEERS

Charles found that Rebecca loved the outdoor life.
And of course he did. Thus when land became available
up the rivers in North Carolina he called a
meeting of the five younger brothers (all except
Isaac, the oldest, and Jacob who was a bonded servant
who was adopted).

"Land is becoming available in North Carolina
and some of us are eligible to receive some of it at no
cost to us."

"How's that?"

"John and I fought alongside other militia men
when we were called on to go to North Carolina to
chase the Indians away. After the third venture to
help the South Carolina governor, Major Maurice
Moore saw some exceptionally good land as he

crossed the Cape Fear River at Rockey Point."

"Charlie," he said, "I got to have me a piece of that there land. You want some too?"

"Wouldn't mind," I said.

He wanted a big chunk of it so got the Federal and Colonial governments to open some of it up to those of us who fought the Indians."

John said, "So now we have to decide if we want to go after some of that land in the wilderness or not. Personally I'm in favor of it. Both Charles and I have been involved in piracy in the past and the authorities might decide to go after us. We'd be easy to find here in Charleston."

Anthony said, "I'm not yet ready to marry but I'd be willing to go up the Cape Fear River and look for land I or any of us might be interested in."

Moses said, "I have no good prospects here in town, so I'd be happy to go for the deep woods."

That left Joseph. He said, "I'm game for looking for land in North Carolina but I plan to stay and live here in town. As with Charles and John, I'm first a mariner and ship captain. I plan to carry on with the business which our family started a hundred or so years ago back in Southeast England."

A few days later, John Florentius Cox, the boy's father, who had retired from the marine life after receiving a severe wound in battle, called the boys back together again. "I hear that there is land up further north in North Carolina where a migrant can claim land in units of fifty acres for himself and any others entering the colony provided he builds a building on the land and plans to live there for a period of five years."

John Jr. asked, "So if Christy and I and our two boys claimed some land we could get 200 acres?"

"That's the way I understand it. Charles could claim five units, two for him and Rebecca and three more for the three children."

"How about us?" Moses asked.

"One unit. That's fifty acres, hardly enough to make it worth while. But I hear that there will soon be some 320 to 400 acre tracts available along the Cape Fear, a whole unit regardless of children."

[Ed. The colonies were seeking out strong young men like the Cox brothers to populate the back woods area, to clear land, to provide bulwarks against the Indian tribes and to build a farming economy.

In the early 1730's John and Charles took the sloops and and sailed up several rivers north of Charleston, then moved off into the swamps and forested lands to hunt and to identify land that might be suitable for homesteading.

Rebecca, seeing Charles come home one day, asked, "You and me, we still a couple?"

"What do you mean?"

"I don't hardly see you except when you want to start another baby."

"It's taken me and John a little time to become well versed in the ways of nature, woods and swamps.

"Also, the county officials over there in North Carolina have a million things they want done and they don't have many people to do them. So me and John, we get stuck with laying out and building roads and setting up ferries to take wagons and carts over rivers."

"That doesn't sound like you are locating good ground for us to plant a tent or build a cabin."

"Well, I'm doing jobs like path finding and exploring the country west into the mountains.

"And John, he's been assigned tasks by the courts, like acting as Justice of the Peace. He even helped some fellow sue me for trespassing on his land. All I did was set up my tent and build a pen for my horses.

"Believe me, as land becomes available along the rivers and streams of North Carolina, Johnny and I will claim our share, big acreage tracts. Right soon now I hope to build a cabin in New Hanover County in an area called Indian Springs."

In the record

1732 - Charles Cox was sued for trespassing - 50 pounds fine.

1732 - Charles Cox ordered to help lay out a road from New River ferry to Cape Fear ferry.

1734 - Onslow County North Carolina was formed from New Hanover County. It adjoins Jones, Carteret, New Hanover and Duplin Counties and is bounded by Core Sound and the Atlantic Ocean.

1735 - John Cox was on a jury in Onslow that found Charles Cox guilty of a second trespassing charge. He was assessed a fine of 20 shillings.

Letter to Martha Cox
John Cox Sr.'s wife, November 1737,
Charleston, South Carolina

Dearest Mother,

Charlie and I just heard about father's new
wound while fighting the Indians in Southern South
Carolina. They say that the venture may have finally
driven the Indians far away from Charleston though.
I hope that is the case.

Christian had a successful birth here in the deep
woods and we now have three very young children
which keeps my sweet wife plenty busy. But as luck
would have it I have been able to acquire land and,
with Charlie's help, have been able to build a small
two room cottage, made with wood cut down from
our own trees.

I have acquired 320 acres on the Cape Fear River
in New Hanover County. The territory here is still
raw and our property is right in the middle of a
swampy area. But it is also a well treed plot with
many Bold Cypress, White Cedars, and Live Oak.
Both of us love it. I have a code identifying it, patent
1662 from book three. It is located near the Cab-
bage Patch Inlet and the Sound.

Fortunately most of the wild Indians had been
driven from coast and problems were primarily those
dealing with battling Mother Nature to acquire
food. There are no towns at this time, only small colonial villages with but a few buildings. The villages

are all on the water so we buy from the passing sea
vessels, pirates, merchants and privateers that sell or
trade food and other goods up and down the Atlantic Coast.

Tell Anthony, Moses and Joseph that this is nice
country and that there is land available right along
the Cape Fear River in 320 to 400 acre chunks. It
would be nice if we all got land adjacent to one another. I think Charlie will get some land soon too.

Love,

Johnny

Joseph Cox
Charleston, South Carolina
1739

Dear Brother,

Just a word to try to keep you informed on what
we are doing out here in the wilderness.

Johnny has moved again. While Johnny was exploring the woods west of the village of Jacksonville,
N. C. he found some richer land. So he has moved to
Onslow County. He plans to settle down, build a log
cabin and become a pillar of the community.

He recently put in a claim on 300 acres of land in
Onslow and also another 200 acres in Craven
County, all in 1739.

- The 300 acres is covered by patent book 5, #

2548, on the west side of **N.W. branch of New River**.

- The 200 acres is covered by patent book 8, # 4230 on the south side of Neuse River below Sappony camp.

I hear that **Anthony has patented 300 ac in Craven County**.

Love from the deep woods,

Charlie

Anthony Cox
October, 1742
Craven County
North Carolina

Dear Brother,

In answer to your questions about John and Charles, they are still at it. They scouted out the land further north, in Onslow County, and finally selected individual sites for building homesteads and raising families. Charles has claimed land in the Richlands area of Onslow County, North Carolina, an appropriate place to raise his family.

1741 - Brothers John and Charles were given Onslow County lands by proving that they had become residents of North Carolina, 50 acres for each person living on the land, including themselves. Charles had five persons and John, four. [Ed. Based on the two men being young enough to go into the wilderness with a young wife and two to three children at home we guess their ages as about thirty five. So we give them birth dates of (b. c1709).]

- By 1741 John Cox Jr. (b c1711) had two boys, Solomon (b. c1732) and John III (b. c1730). [Ed. Fourth John Cox in line from Captain John Cox of Bermuda.]

- By 1741 Charles and Rebecca Cox had three children, Charles Jr. (b. c1733), Moses Jr. (b. c1735), and Aaron (b. c1737).

- Also in 1741 - Edward Marshburn - 150 ac Onslow.

- Charles Cox - 600 ac Duplin.

- Charles Cox - 200 ac Onslow. This land was patented by Charles per book 8, #4257 and is located on the **S.W. side of New River between John Glover's land and John Williams, joining a branch of the river**.

- 1741, Charles Cox was on the tax rolls for both New Hanover and Onslow Counties. In the same year John was on the roll for Onslow.

- 1741, Also Charles Cox obtained a patent for **640 acres in Onslow County, book 5, # 2581, on the N.W. Branch of New River above Dutchman's Branch**.

- 1742, (County deed book) Aug. 4, **Charles Cox of Indian Grove, New Hanover County, North Carolina,** sold for 150 pounds, 200 acres on New River in Onslow County, joining John Glover and John Williams. [Ed. See 1741, patent 4257.]

I trust that the foregoing will bring you up to date on your brothers' real estate adventures.

Kind regards,

Brother Joseph Cox

Christmas 1742
Brothers Cox and sons,
Deep in the Woods of
North Carolina

Journal Entry Letter by Joseph Cox, December 1742

During the past few years our family has been engaged in events which I have chosen to record in my journal in which I, from time to time, do record events which I consider significant.

In 1739 South Carolina found it expedient to raise a force to assist General James Oglethorpe in an invasion of Florida. I contacted you all and brought the conflict to your attention. As a group we enlisted with the Crown Colony to support the invasion of Saint Augustine through use of our two sloops. We determined that we should sign on as privateers with Lettres-of-Marque from the governor.

Armed with the letters we sent the two ships to sea, one captained by John Cox with Anthony as Lieutenant and the other captained by Charles with Moses as Lieutenant. We recruited some thirty men for each craft promising to pay each mariner based on sharing any prize vessel captured.

Our two sloops ventured onto the ocean and sailed off the shore some twenty miles out, venturing westward from time to time to check for Spanish or French flagged vessel.

Initially we had no effect on Oglethorpe's attack on Saint Augustine as it was manned from the mainland. The general managed to tire his troops by marching up and down the poor interior roads and making other blunders. After wasting considerable time the expedition was withdrawn as the hurricane season came into being and wicked storms drove the troops back to Charles Towne.

We continued to send our two sloops into action until 1742, taking several frigates and other small Spanish merchant vessels as prizes each year, but striking no gold bullion.

August 1742 - During our time at sea we managed to sight one of the Spanish convoys where they were taking care of about twenty large galleons using another twenty five ships for guards.

Being smaller than the Spanish vessels we could flit into the midst of the fleet and then scoot out again with but little fire against us. Ultimately we cut a ship loose from the others. But we hadn't time to board her before a fleet of Spanish war ships came into sight over the horizon.

The Spanish had a powerful fleet with several thousand marines ready for action. When they looked as though they were about to attack St. Simon Georgia, John and Charles sailed up the Georgia coast to Charles Towne and notified the governor. He sent a strong force of land troops and began marching (and riding on our sloops) toward St. Simon Harbor.

The Spanish thought that our two vessels, flying the English Union Jack, was a forerunner to an English fleet. The Spanish embarked on their ships and set sail for Cuba.

It was believed that if the Dons had taken St. Simon that they would have aroused the Indians and slaves into an insurrection against the colonies.

Joseph Cox
Charles Towne, South Carolina

FOURTEEN

CAPE FEAR RIVER

[The Cape Fear River patenting process was unique in that it came about in a way to benefit Maurice Moore, a member of the dominant political family in Charleston.]

War with the Indians, as told by John Cox

In 1711 there was a massacre of the white population in the Albemarle area by the Tuscarora Indians. 130 colonists were butchered.

A group of the colonists were warned by one of the Coree group of Indians and so managed to congregate on one plantation, that of John Shackleford, near Beaufort, and with the help of pirates, repulse an attack in that area.

Even so, the Indians would have wiped out the white population but for the timely and generous as-

sistance of South Carolina. When the governor of
North Carolina requested help from his two sister
colonies, Virginia and South Carolina, Virginia refused to help. But Governor Moore of South Carolina never hesitated. He sent a force of 4,000 troops,
colonists, etc. without a promise to pay.

Several years later, Colonel James Moore, son of
the governor, headed up a second unit of militia.
And finally, Major Maurice Moore, another brother
of James Moore lead a third force. The South Caro-
linians were victorious and Major Maurice Moore
stayed in North Carolina, becoming involved in land
dealings and in the politics surrounding the management of the colony.

When leading his troops into central North Carolina to fight the aroused Indians, he had noted, when
marching along the coast and crossing the Cape
Fear River, how pleasant the land, trees and vegeta-
tion were. He fell in love with the area and resolved
to live there.

The Lords Proprietors, a group of English noblemen who managed the Carolinas and the Somers Islands, also liked the river area. They had prohibited
settlements within 20 miles of the river.

In 1725 Major Maurice Moore and a hundred
friends from Albemarle pushed the colony into selling Cape Fear River land. The major obtained a
tract of several thousand acres but it wasn't till 1737
that land became available to other colonists.

But the major was able to lay out the roads and
economic sections of a new town called Brunswick.
Immediately there was trade from the interior and
the town grew until regular shipping runs were under

way by 1731.

Trade...Number of Merchants...Rich Planters...42 vessels visited the city in 1731.

Brunswick was organized in 1725, in Carteret County which county was established in 1722.

Some of the original land grants were patented in New Hanover County. Brunswick land was registered in Beaufort, the Center of Carteret County.

Efforts were made during this period to publicize the availability of land in the Cape Fear River area as well as the land open for patent further upriver.

One plantation on the river was said to be using three ships, two sloops and a brigantine, all loaded with lumber for delivery to the West Indies.

Across the river to the southwest were Indian villages. The tribesmen were raising fine corn, likewise wheat and hemp.

But on the northeast side of the river there were many very big swamps. There were also big lakes and lots of wild animals such as deer, wild turkeys, doves, squirrels, geese, ducks, rabbits and of course fish. As one moved away from the river and further northwest the woods were filled with hardwood, walnut, hickory, ash, hard maple and various types of oak.

Major Maurice Moore drove the Indians from the area near Brunswick in 1725.

[Ed. Interesting enough, some of Major Bonnet's men escaped capture on Sept. 18, 1718. They were thought to have gone up the river and amalgamated with the Indians on the Lumber River. After the permanent settlement started in 1725, it was found that in the Cape Fear River area a considerable number of the prior settlers already spoke English.]

We various brothers Cox served in the South Carolina militia and as soon as we could we patented land
in New Hanover and along the New and the Neuse
Rivers (in the 1730's and 40's)

Patenting Land

1737 - **John Cox** was the first of the brethren
to patent land in North Carolina, acquiring **320
acres on the Cape Fear River** in New Hanover
County in 1737 when the territory was still raw and
covered by swamp and rain forest. (From patent
book 3, # 1662 and referenced Cabbage Inlet and
Sound)

[Ed. The Cox brothers acquired other lands near
Turkey Creek in Lower Onslow County in the
1740's. When Cape Fear River land became available they each patented 400 acre sections. Brothers
Joseph and Anthony, living in Charleston, also acquired patents on 400 acre parcels. Joseph in his will
of c1761 left 300 acres of this land to Charles Cox's
son Moses Jr.]

Wilmington
(Continuation of John Cox's Journal Entry)

On the 20th of November, 1740, our militia was
attached to a force under Captain James Innes. We

left Wilmington to fight the Spanish at Cartegena. Things went badly for us and many of our force died from illnesses brought on by the mosquito infested swamps and the water in northern South America.

We accomplished nothing and few of us returned.

The next year, 1741 and again in 1744 and 1747 Spanish privateers cruised the coast and raided our sea ports along the sand islands. In 1744 they entered our harbor and took possession of Beaufort. In 1744 they sailed up the Cape Fear River until Captain James Simpson and a fleet of small merchant vessels ran one Spanish vessel aground on a sand bar. We then took this vessel as a prize. The other ships were driven off.

In 1748 we built a fort at Brunswick. We then had little trouble with the Indians until the French started the French & Indian War in 1754. Captain Dimes of Wilmington was, in 1754, appointed the Commander of all the American forces in the French and Indian War with Lieutenant George Washington reporting to him.

in the record

1743 - **Charles Cox** - 400 ac N. Hanover. This land was identified on patent book 5, # 2933 in 1745 as on the **East side of N.E. Branch of Cape Fear River**, joining a small branch, Joe Hulebrans and a great swamp. [Ed. This land was likely upriver from John's patent in 1737.]

- 1743 - Joseph Cox - 400 ac N. Hanover.- 400 acres N. Hanover. on the East side of the NE branch of Cape Fear River beginning in the low ground of the River.")

[Ed. From the Sampson-Duplin Deeds Book:]

(For the land left by Joseph to his nephew, Moses Cox, son of Charles, Joseph's brother.)

Dated 12 July 1779. Thirty pounds proclamation money for 300 acres "On the East side of the North East Branch of Cape Fear River beginning ... in the low ground of the river, (Part of a greater tract granted to Joseph Cox by patent dated 26 July 1743.)"

FIFTEEN

JOSEPH

A Joseph Journal Entry, July 1739

I may be the youngest amongst my several youngest brothers all born before 1720. So my turn at seeking out land in North Carolina came late in the cycle. Although I did patent my 400 acres of land along the Cape Fear River before Anthony, who may have been third eldest among we five.

Being born late, it has befallen me to be the brother that stayed at home. So I still live in Charleston, South Carolina, on Church Street, where our father raised us in the house he obtained when he retired from the sea.

And it is from here that I carry on the family's old line of business as a mariner. My wife, the former Hannah Liston, manages the firm's finances, handling payrolls, payables and paying, in cash, employees and suppliers. She also maintains records and prepares shipping documentation. Without her help

I'd never have been able to keep the business going.

Charles, our oldest brother, (b. 1709), loves the outdoor life. He sails our two sloops and takes the bigger one when he is off privateering. But he has found that privateering is turning him and his crew into pirates, not such a good thing. Thus he resolved to look for land in North Carolina. He seems to want to migrate along one of the rivers into the interior of the North American continent.

He talked the idea over with Rebecca, John and the rest of us, including me and our father, John. We all agreed to look for land and to advise one another of any that could be available.

Thus in the mid 1730's Charles and John, the two oldest of the five brothers, took our smaller sloop to test the waters and land of the several rivers emptying into the Atlantic from southern North Carolina.

Since 1737, when brother John patented 320 acres along the Cape Fear River, N.H. County, Cabbage Inlet and the Sound, the boys have taken to leaving their new families here in town with me. I act as their surrogate father. Hannah and I can only leave them alone and watch them grow. At least they get more care than me and my brothers did when we lived with our grandfather on Bermuda.

#

A 1741 letter from Charlie (b. 1709)

Joseph Cox
Charleston, South Carolina
September 20, 1741

My Dearest Brother,

Just a word to try to keep you informed on what we are doing out here in the wilderness.

John is out looking for more land again. While he was exploring the woods west of the village of Jacksonville, N. C. he found some very rich land where the black dirt extends two to three feet deep. So he has moved his search for land to Onslow County. Soon he will be settling down, building a log cabin and becoming a justice of the peace.

He recently put in a claim on 300 acres of land in Onslow and also another for 200 acres in Craven County, all in 1739. Craven County is further north and is drained by the Neuse River. I'll probably look at that area too although I think I prefer Onslow.

- The 300 acres is covered by patent book 5, # 2548, on the west side of **N.W. branch of New River**.
- The 200 acres is covered by patent book 8, # 4230 on the **south side of Neuse River below Sappony camp**.

Love from the deep woods,

Charlie

A 1748 Journal Entry of Joseph's

Early in 1743 Charlie found two adjacent pieces of land on the Cape Fear of 400 acres each. Together we went into the Land Office and signed our life away for this patent land.

I have done a few things having to do with the dark woods and land patenting but not so much as John and Charlie. In 1743 I joined Charles in patenting land on the Cape Fear River. You'll notice that my patent identifies my land using the same description as does Charlie's patent.

But my job is to keep our current business alive. I haven't been back to the woods since 1743.

Our oldest brother, Isaac, has long concerned himself with the our business in Philadelphia and New York. He is doing well in his own right. We seem to be losing touch with him.

#

A 1752 Moses Journal Entry about Joseph

Brother Joseph Sr. married Hannah Liston in St. Philips Ch., Charleston, S.C., 3 July 1746.

Joseph was about 26 years old at this time. Besides obtaining land along the Cape Fear River, along with Charles, John, Anthony (b. 1713) and me (Moses (b. 1717), Joseph (b. 1720), by 1752, had sons John (b. c1750) and Joseph Jr. (b c1750).

Charles Cox
Onslow County, 1753

Dearest Brother Charlie,

I went and done it. Bought lot #204 in town for 215 pounds currency and have had a house built on it. The address is Joe Cox, Mariner, New Church Street, Charleston, South Carolina.

But, and here's my sad story. The Gods didn't like it; they sent us a big hurricane of November blew the damn house over, breaking it into pieces and carrying much of it away either to the sea or off to wherever. Fortunately we had taken refuge in St. John's Church nearby and were not killed.

Issac who now has possession of our old house down the way has insisted that we stay with him till we rebuild a new structure on our old location. It's nice to have a good brother.

If you see any of our other brothers out in the woods, let them know that we're safe. I miss you all.

Love,

Joseph Cox
Charleston, South Carolina.

Charles Cox
Onslow County, North Carolina
October, 1765

Dear Brother, Charlie,

Thought you might want to know that Isaac has bought lot # 104 in Charleston with the money he got from selling our old house. The price was 1400 pounds.

Isaac is spending a good portion of his time in New York now so I'm not sure what he intends to do with the lot. But I witnessed the lot transaction.

By the way, what do you expect to do with that 400 acre tract you have on the Cape Fear? Is young Moses interested in moving there? If so I might deed part of my next door plot over to him. My boys don't seem to enjoy the outdoor life enough to want to put a cabin on the land.

Your brother,

Joseph Cox

Notes about Joseph's sons:

John, taxes Duplin, 1783. Will goods to Joseph. Hillsbury Dist., Continential Line

Joseph Jr., taxes Duplin, 1783 - in militia, 1778 muster roll, 2nd N.C., Hillsbury District, Continential Line.

SIXTEEN

JOHN

A John Cox Journal Entry,

In the early 1730's Charles and I, began searching for land in the Carolinas in earnest. I was born in 1711 and Charles in 1709. In the late 1720's and early 1730's we five boys spent the summers living with our grandfather Florentius Cox at his home on Bermuda. We spent the winters at home on Church Street in Charleston attending school and helping out at our parents' business on the docks. We learned the boat building business and the ship seafaring business while Joseph learned the merchandising business (buying and selling).

In 1731 We took the sloop, *Candy*, and and sailed up the **Cape Fear River** and **New River** north of Charleston, then moved off into the swamps and forested lands to hunt and to identify land that might be suitable for homesteading.

The colonies were seeking out strong young men like me and my brothers to populate the back woods area, to clear land, to provide bulwarks against the Indian tribes and to build a farming economy.

Charlie and I became well versed in the ways of nature, woods and swamps. At first we merged with the colonists ahead of us and took on assignments of path finding and exploring the country west into the mountains.

And then we were assigned tasks by the courts, acted as Justices of the Peace, sued and were sued in turn, and helped build the first roads in the county.

In 1735 I was assigned jury duty and in fact had to rule against my brother Charles when he was tried for trespassing on another settler's land near Brunswick. He and I were without much in the way of funds. When night fell on the community, old Charlie just took off and found himself a quiet spot beneath some hard wood trees and laid himself down and went to sleep. He could have been charged with vagrancy but he had some money in his pockets so the constable charged him with trespassing.

I tried to get off his jury by saying that he was my brother. Because we were short on jurors the J.P. merely had me promise to be fair and honest. Charlie ended up paying a fine.

As land became available along the rivers and streams of North Carolina, the two of us claimed big acreage tracts.

In 1737 I signed up for a 400 acre section along the Cape Fear River, about forty miles upriver from Brunswick. We built us a cabin: moved in, brought our girl friends and later our wives and small chil-

dren into the forests. Our address was an area
known as Indian Springs and Indian Mounds, in
New Hanover County. The Indians that had occupied the acreage had been chased away by the English and the colonists back in 1725.

We immediately began clearing the land and in
the fall planted some winter wheat. We continued
clearing the land all winter until we had another five
acres available for truck farm types of vegetables
and corn. The first summer we had lots of problems
with wild animals wanted to nibble at our blossoms.
But we stayed at it until we had enough produce to
sell and to store for the winter. We were now able to
buy a couple of horses, warm blankets and a steel
plough.

Meantime, I took *Candy*, our small sloop and
went up the nearby New River. This river was not so
wide as the Cape Fear River but it flowed steadily
along with trees on either side. In 1739 I was granted
a 300 acre tract of land on N.W. Branch of New
River at Smith's Creek.

In 1739 I was also elected a J.P. along with John
Starkey and Ed Mashburn, men from families that
would in future years intermarry with the Coxes.

#

Joseph Cox
Charleston, South Carolina, 1739
About John

Dear Joe,

Just a word to try to keep you informed on what John is doing out here in the wilderness.

He has moved again.

While John was exploring the woods west of the village of Jacksonville, N. C. he found some richer and less swampy land. So he has moved to Onslow County, settling down, building a better cabin and becoming a justice of the peace.

He recently put in a claim on 300 acres of land in Onslow and also another 200 acres in Craven County, all in 1739.

- The 300 acres is covered by patent book 5, # 2548, on the west side of **N.W. branch of New River.**

- The 200 acres is covered by patent book 8, # 4230 on the **south side of Neuse River below Sappony camp.-**

Also, John was awarded a brand for his farm animals. I already had a brand from 1735.

John is now a Justice of the Peace.

Love from the deep woods,

Charlie

Anthony Cox
Craven County,
North Carolina, October 1744

Dear Tony,

In answer to your questions about John and
Charles, they are still at it. They scouted out the land
further north, in Onslow County, and finally selected
individual sites for building homesteads and raising
families. Charles claimed land in the Richlands area
of Onslow County, North Carolina, an appropriate
place to raise his family.

1741 - Brothers John and Charles were given Onslow County lands by proving that they had become
residents of North Carolina, 50 acres for each person
living on the land, including themselves. Charles had
five persons and John, four.

By 1741 John Cox (b 1711) had two boys, Solomon (b. c1737) and John IV (b. c1735). [Ed. Fourth
John Cox in line from Captain John Cox of Bermuda.]

I trust that the foregoing will bring you up to date
on your brothers real estate adventures.

Kind regards,

Joe

18 April, 1743 - John Cox's Will (b. c1711)

The Will of John Cox was witnessed by John
Starkey, John Cox's wife, Christian Cox and a
daughter, Martha - 100 ac Onslow.

Other land had already been assigned to sons John
IV and Solomon. [Ed. Note that this John (b. c1711)
was named after his father while he named his only
daughter, Martha, after his mother, Martha.] Solomon was named after his wife's father.

in the record

1735 - John Cox on jury duty. Found Charles
guilty.

1737 - John Cox, 320 acres, Cape Fear River,
New Hanover County, Cabbage Inlet Sound joining
J. Husband, ye head of a small creek.

1739 - John Cox, 300 acres, Onslow County. West
side of N.W. Branch of New River joining Smith's
Creek and Richard Williams.

1739 - John Cox, 200 acres in Craven County.

1739 - John Cox acquired a brand.

1740 - John Cox for 299 pounds sold to John Por-
ter 300 acres on New Topsail Sound called
Freeman's Hammock.

1741 - John Cox, proved rights, 4 people, 200
acres, Duplin County

1743 - John Cox - 200 acres Onslow County.

1743 - John Cox will.

1744 - John Starkey sold 347 acres of John Cox's
land as part of settling the John Cox estate.

SEVENTEEN

CHARLES

A Charles Journal Entry

I, Charles, was born just after the turn of the century, on the Island of Bermuda, the eldest of the final five children of John and Martha Cox. John, my father, after a severe wound incurred while fighting against Spanish privateers, moved to Charleston and began living a life "on the beach."

For much of my growing up period I, along with my brothers, lived on the Island of Bermuda with my grandfather, Florentius Cox. He lived on the family's original land, some fifty acres, fronting on the ocean in the community of Devonshire. We boys spent much of our time on the sea in vessels owned by my grandfather and used by him to carry produce from the island to ports along the North American coast for trading purposes.

We sailed with my grandfather on such voyages and as we got older, like 12 or 15, my brothers and I sailed the small ocean going sloops back to Nassau in the Bahamas where we interacted with many buccaneers, mariners and pirates. John Jr. (Johnny) and I crewed with some of the desperadoes.

When I was old enough, my father tried to get me to quit the sea and to come help him out in Charleston. I would have helped manage the shipping and merchandising business which he operated from there as a cog in the Cox family's business centered in Canterbury, England.

Whenever John Jr., Tony or I would show up at home, between sea ventures, grandfather would talk to us of other ventures which were opening up in North Carolina. He sent us on exploration trips up one or the other of the three rivers which emptied into the Atlantic, up the coast from Charleston, Cape Fear River, New River, and Neuse River.

In the early 1730's John Jr., Tony and I moved our base of land operations to the area near Brunswick, New Hanover County, near the river. We soon found ourselves involved in fighting the Indians, chasing them out of the community such that Brunswick could become incorporated as a Village.

#

In the record

1732 - Charles Cox sued for trespassing - 50

pounds.

1732 - Charles Cox ordered to lay out road from New River ferry to Cape Fear ferry.

1735 - Charles Cox found guilty of trespassing and assessed a fine of 20 shillings.

1736 - While out on the Atlantic, between here and Bermuda, my crew and I, sailing our larger sloop, chanced to find a Spanish merchant vessel drifting apart from its protecting galleons. It had its own protection, twenty cannon on each side but it could not fire on us because we kept our vessel to the galleons stern or bow. On board I found a young lady all filled with anger. I took her home to Charleston, eventually marrying her. Her name was Rebecca O'Brien, daughter of a Spanish Admiral.

#

Johnny (John Jr.), Tony and I continued searching the deep woods west and north of the new town for land to claim. At the time we were both in our twenties, not too well versed in the ways of either man or nature. But we were quick learners.

We sailed our smaller sloop, *Candy*, up the sounds, into the mouths and then up the **New River**. We wanted to find land that was way back in the outback behind the water affected land near the sea. We wanted rich land with black earth and with fresh water available both for the crops and also as a way to ship product from our planting ground to the sea for market. Our oldest brother Isaac was now taking over much of our father's marine business

with Philadelphia. We planned that he would take
our produce to the markets up north to New York,
Philadelphia and Boston Town.

#

1737 - Johnny has gotten to know the local politi-
cians and has patented 400 acres of land right up the
Cape Fear River. I'm helping him build a cabin and
we will share it when living in the area.

1741 - Johnny (John Jr.) and I have been allotted
Onslow County lands by proving that we had become residents of North Carolina, 50 acres for each
person living on the land, including themselves. I
had five persons and John, four.

1741 - Charles Cox - 600 ac Duplin County. Duplin is in the area between New River and Cape Fear
River.

- John Starkey - Carteret County, proved rights

- Charles Cox - 200 ac Onslow. This land was patented by me per book 8, #4257 and is located on the
**S.W. side of New River between John Glover's
land and John Williams, joining a branch of the
river.**

[Ed. Charles was about 32 years old at this time,
old enough to go into the wilderness with a young
wife and three children.]

- 1741 - **640 acres in Onslow County, book 5,
2581, on the N.W. Branch of New River
above Dutchman's Branch.**

\#

A Charles Journal Entry 1741

Our 640 acre patent is great. Rebecca and I agree that this tract of land will be our home for the rest of our lives. The dirt is solid black and it is about two feet deep. Our property is right on the river with a large site for building our dock and storage bins for crops to be shipped to the sea. Further on up the river and still on our property is a good site for us to build a gristmill where we can process our grain and that of our neighbors.

Seventeen forty one has been a very good year for us. We've moved our little family to our own long term home site; while yet being able to acquire several other sites here and in adjacent counties. Young Moses is living with Rebecca and me for the moments but I expect he will move to his own estate soon.

\#

In the records - 1742-1771

1742 - (County deed book) Aug. 4, **Charles Cox of Indian Grove, New Hanover County, North Carolina,** sold for 150 pounds, 200 acres on New River in Onslow County, joining John Glover and John Williams. [Ed. See 1741, patent 4257.] (Note: having the 640 acre tract I no longer need these 200 acres.)

1743 - Both Joseph and I acquired 400 acres along the Cape Fear River near John's . I helped Joseph build the required cabin and we two used the 800 acres as our private hunting preserve after John died late in the year. For the next several years we hunted the land for bears, deer, black panthers, wild turkeys, doves, pheasants, rabbits and squirrels. Later Moses and Anthony joined us for a weeks hunting in the fall just after harvest time.

[Ed. The Cape Fear River location is good for transport purposes but the water is brackish. For some years the English government would not even allow settlers to claim land close to the river.]

in the record

1745 - Charles sold for 150 pounds, 200 acres on Cattail Branch at Jethro Mashburne's corner, being called Brown's Tract. Also 200 acres on Dutchman's Branch.

1746 - Charles was a witness to sale of land on NW branch of New River at Jethro Mashburne's line. Probably same land he sold in 1745 (on Cattail Branch).

1751 - Charles witnessed a sale of 150 acres on **Older Branch on NW branch of New River to John Jarman. [Note that the Jarmans lived adjacent to the Coxes in the Richlands area.]**

1753 - Charles patented 300 acres on Turkey Creek book 2, # 432.

1753 - **Charles, a carpenter, sold 300 acres on a fork of Turkey Creek,** joining Peter Poory.

Charles Cox's Will

1771 - will - Charles Cox Sr. to wife Rebecca and to children:
> Charles Cox Jr., married Hannah
> Jasper (Jesse) Cox
> Susannah, married Arthur Royal
> Sarah, married Nathaniel Jones
> > Also John Boston
> Moses Cox Jr. (the younger) married,
> > 1st, Hannah Williams and
> > 2nd, Elizabeth Foyle
> > > Aaron, married Mary, daughter of
> > > Hardy Gregory

1772 - Moses Cox Jr. and Aaron Cox (sons of Charles Sr.) executors of estate of Charles Cox (d 1771).

1777 - Charles Cox Sr., whose will was signed in 1771, included in his estate his original 640 acres plus 100 acres next to it, plus an Arthur Royal patent for 120 acres. Test Jesse Ballard.

EIGHTEEN

MOSES Sr. of Dobbs County

A Moses Cox Sr. Journal Entry

I was born in about 1710, the fourth in line of the last five boys, sons of John Cox, Sr. of Bermuda, now living on Church Street in Charleston. Now I have began serving as captain of one of the Cox family's sloops carrying goods back and forth from Charleston to Bermuda to Philadelphia.

Before I was ten, I went along when we boys began spending a good part of each year with Grandfather Florentius on Bemuda. But the old gentleman would not let me go along when John Jr. and Charles began taking one or the other of the sloops on pleasure trips.

Grandfather said, "You're too young."

I insisted, "I can serve on a sloop and help sail it straight."

He said, "Your brothers may go to Nassau."

So why can't I go too?

"Like I said. You're too young."

"Always it's because I'm too young. When will I be old enough?"

"Maybe never if you keep pestering me."

And so my too older brothers went off to do their own thing in the Bahamas, at Nassau, where the bottom dregs of the sea robbers of the Caribbean held forth. And they were eligible to be hung on sight.

And then it was my son, Solomon, (son of Moses Sr.) who asked me one day, "What more did grandfather do about you five brothers?"

"Well Florentius Cox, my grandfather, found the five of us boys really difficult to handle. He set me down and taught me to play chess."

Solomon asked, "Did we boys, sons of the younger sons of John Sr. take after their fathers and grandfather?"

I said, "I'm one of the fathers."

Son Solomon, said, "I know. And all of you have been men of the sea, bound to ply the trade as sailors and pirates and bound to get into fights with buccaneers over the lease little thing.

Solomon asked, "You never went with John Jr. and Charles?"

"Not for years. I finally got to go along when John and Charles went off to search for home sites in the deep woods of Eastern North Carolina."

Solomon asked, "But you didn't become a pirate?"

"No," I said to my son. "I proposed to my brothers Charles, John Jr., and Anthony, that I would keep one or the other of them company. I helped them work their new farm land, harvest the crops and deliver same to Brunswick and Wilmington.

"And I sailed back to visit Joseph in Charleston. I captained one of the sloops now and again, living with Joe and the family on Church Street.

"In 1741 I was living with Charlie, his wife and the first two of their children in New Hanover in a small log house on a patent at Indian Grove."

One rainy evening Charles, dripping wet, came in through the door. He called to Rebecca, his wife, "I've found us a big site further up country from here."

"Oh Charlie. Will this be our last move?"

"Probably. The new patent has 640 acres in an area called RichLands, on New River, Onslow County."

"RichLands?"

"The soil is a soft and black and it's at least three feet deep."

"My heavenly days!"

Charlie looked at me, "Moses, you help me build a cottage on the site and I'll give you this land we're on and the cottage, 400 acres, on the Cape Fear River. And I'll name a my next son after you, Moses Jr."

And so it was that I helped Charlie and Rebecca clear a home site and build a beginning log cabin with two rooms and an outdoor kitchen. I watched over the children from time to time and when I could I hunted for more free, or nearly free, land of my own in Dobbs County, up New River to the west. I was also on the lookout for a bride.

[Ed. The Onslow County Heritage Book has a quote that states, "I believe **Charles Cox had another brother, Moses who came to Lenoir-Dobbs County about the same time. The court house there burned, however, and we know little of him.**"]

Dobbs County went out of existence in the 1790's and the southern part of it has been called Lenoir since that time.

In the spring of 1742 just as I passed the twenty five year old mark, I found a genteel lady, Dorothy Denny, from my parish in Charleston who looked on me with favor. Before long we were married and she was accompanying me to my 400 acres and log cabin along the Cape Fear River at Indian Grove. I found more land available along the upper reaches of New River and put in for rights to some of it. I have recently split part of it with my two boys, Solomon and Andrew.

More Moses Sr. Journal Entry Material

In 1745 I helped Charles build a gristmill and began to take my limited crops of mill produce there for grinding and bagging. The mill is the biggest thing built by human hands out here in the deep woods. The local Indians come over when Charles runs the gristmill. They enjoy watching as the water drives the big waterwheel.

In the records

1745 - **Onslow County** - Moses Cox Sr. witnessed a sale of land on Buck's Branch.

1747 - **Onslow County** - Moses Cox Sr. a witness to sale of land between Humphry on south side of N.W. branch of New River on swamp side.

1752 - A hurricane destroyed the courthouse in New Hanover County and most of the records were lost.

1754 - Moses Cox Sr. on roster of Onslow County militia for the French and Indian War.

1769 taxpayers - **Dobbs County** - Moses Cox Sr. Solomon and Andrew Cox, (b. c1743), sons of Moses. [Ed. Dobbs is further west from Onslow along New River and north of New Hanover and Cape Fear River. It was formed in 1758 from Johnson County. In 1795 it was broken up into two counties, Lenoir and Green.]

1769 taxpayers list - **Onslow County** - Moses Cox Sr.

1769 taxpayers - Dobbs County - Arthur Cox, John Cox, (b. c1735), son of John, (b. c1711) and John Jr. (b. c1755), all Dobbs County.

1776 - 81 - 2nd N.C. , Revolutionary War.

1776 - 1778 - Andrew and Solomon were in the Dobbs County militia. That militia went to the relief of Charleston and was right in the middle of the fighting when the British fleet first attacked.

They were taken prisoner and held captive after the battle of Kings Mountain in 1780 but were traded for Tories taken prisoner by the 2nd North

Carolina forces in the year 1778.

1780 - Andrew taxpayer in Dobbs County. Dobbs was replaced by Greene and Lenoir Counties.

THE FRENCH AND INDIAN WAR

[Ed. From 1730 to 1800 America was in an expansion mode, and the colonists from the eastern sea coasts began to move westward to the eastern slopes of the Appalachian mountains. This began with the opening of land in New Hanover, Onslow and Dobbs Counties in the 1740's and pushed gradually west from where hearty pioneers headed into the Indian held forests at the headwaters of the rivers emptying into the Atlantic Ocean from Pennsylvania to Georgia.

Solomon asked me, "Father Moses, where were you during the French and Indian war?"

"I was one of the young men who ventured to the mountains to trade with the Indians. In about 1750 we traders began to work with better support from the English.

"Historically we were now approaching the great battle between the English against both France and Spain for predominance in North America.

"My work now forced me to leave Dorothy, my young wife, and you two boys in North Carolina as I went beyond the blue mountains to the west to find furs which I could bring to Charleston where brother Joseph could merchandise them for cash money.

"As a leading trader with the Indians to the west I

mixed with and talked with the English garrisoning the thin line of red-coated soldiers along the coasts and near where English oceangoing vessels would load and unload cargo.

"I talked with a British Major."

I said, "There are a lot more French out there."

The British officer asked, "Do they harm you?"

I answered, "Not if I find out that they are there before they are aware of me. I run and hide."

Major Mallone laughed, "Ha, ha. You fear them?"

"They have the Indians on their side.

Major Mallone asked, "Why is that?"

"The Indians are accustomed to dealing with the French. Often the Frenchman lives among them. He has often married an Indian lass. Or he might be a half breed himself."

Major Mallone asked, "What do you want of us?"

"It would be nice if I could see as many English soldiers in the woods as there are French soldiers."

"We have to maintain garrisons all over the world."

I pleaded, "Just a few soldiers in the forests?"

"We have to worry about trade on the high sea."

I said, "If we don't bring in hides to trade from the forests you won't have much business from here."

Major Mallone, in charge of the garrison at Charleston, got me aside one day. "Moses, you know, about that support you wanted in the deep woods?"

"Yes?"

"I think you'll soon have it."

In 1752 I was on duty as scout for the British at a post at Pickwillany when a party of Indians led by a French trader broke up the post and burned the buildings to the ground. I had been forewarned of the impending attack so that I and most of the garrison escaped with our lives.

I then reported back to Major Mallone at Charleston. I said, "We had virtually no soldier support and the Indians were all on the French side."

"Any other ideas?"

"Send a force. Wipe out a town or two. Show them that the British have a strong right arm."

Major Mallone said, "The Indians will be quiet now."

"But the French won't. They are building other forts on Lake Erie, on the Mississippi and on French Creek."

The Major said, "We will have to repel force by force."

[Ed. In 1753 Robert Dinwiddle, the governor of Virginia, decided to warn the French to get out of the western area of Virginia. He selected Captain George Washington to deliver the message.]

George Washington was joined by an adventurer, Christopher Gist, and by me, now a Lieutenant. I was a member of the colonial militia. With us and two Indian scouts, Washington pushed on to the forks of the Ohio River. There, we had conferences with Indians, with the French agent, Joncaire and with the commandant at Fort Le Boeuf. He gave us a flat negative reply, "We will not leave."

After the negative reaction from the French and Indians, I contacted my British Major friend at Charleston.

I told him, "Major, the French seem to be getting ready for a stronger battle."

"And our side?"

"That's hard to say. But I've been told to report for duty with Washington again."

"Whereabouts?"

"By the forks on the Ohio River."

I reported to Major Mallone, "Sir, at the forks, the French quickly pushed out our small English and colonial force sent to hold the position. When Washington arrived, he got our forces in line and promptly moved ahead to retake the ground already lost.

"We then fell in with a group of the French who were out reconnoitering. Our men killed the French commander and the French dispersed.

"But we were later defeated by a strong detachment from Fort Duquense. The French took our arms and let us go."

Back at Charleston, I wrote a letter to the British government explaining what had happened in the frontier skirmish. I asked for further support.

I reported to Major Mallone in 1755. "My brothers, Charles and Joseph, and I are now part of a North Carolina militia unit sent on temporary duty to support the British under General Braddock, a hard nosed British officer."

"Keep me posted Moses."

I reported to the major, "On July 9th our expedition was attacked by a force of French and Indians. The British officers fought bravely but they refused to modify their tactics to meet those of the Indians. George Washington, an American on Braddock's staff, did well with the militia, but the defeat was overwhelming."

Major Mallone asked, "You and your brothers were taken captive?"

"No Sir. About a dozen of us escaped into the woods."

Mallone asked, "Couldn't the Indians have found you?"

"All was confusion. We took canoes which the Indians had cached and which we found."

"So now the British controled area which had been advancing westward is now pushed back east to the mountains again?"

"Yes, the French and Indians have control."

Later in the year Major Mallone called me to him. He said, "William Pitt has become Prime Minister of Great Britain and the English are expected to carry their war with the French to the heart of the enemy's positions here in North America; west of the mountains."

In 1757, I talked further with Major Mallone. I told him, "Our forces have captured the French forts at Frontenac under Lieutenant-Colonel Bradstreet (we call them light colonels) and Duquesne (renamed Pittsburgh after William Pitt)."

Major Mallone said, "Elsewhere the British are active too. Our forces have captured Quebec, in

Canada, under the leadership of Admiral Saunders and General Wolfe. Also we have captured the French post of Niagara on the Great Lakes."

Major Mallone and I were talking as 1760 drew to a close. The Major said, "In the first part of the year, the English took Montreal and now France has surrendered all of Canada."

"How did Pitt feel about that?"

"He now wanted to attack the Spanish treasure fleet. But he was overruled by the new King, George III who wanted to improve relations with Spain.

"Pitt resigned his post as Secretary of State in protest."

I asked, "Are the Spanish and the English joining forces now?"

"Yes. The French and Indian War now includes the Spanish and the British, as allies. We hope to take Cuba next."

"I've heard that the colonists will support the English venture. We plan to use our two sloops, now carrying war cannons, to carry American militia from mainland ports to Havana."

Major Mallone said, "In the meantime we British hope to take nother Spanish possession, Manila."

NINETEEN

ANTHONY, New Hanover / Craven Counties

An Anthony Journal Entry - 1736

I, Anthony (Tony), am the center aged of the five youngest Cox brothers in our family. mentioned in John Cox's will where he cautioned the oldest brother Isaac, and the stay at home, Joseph, to care for their mother. They were also to use the income from the house in Charleston, North Carolina to educate or train the five younger boys until they all reached the age of twenty one. We five were born sequentially about as follows:

Charles Sr. (Charlie) 1709,
John Jr. (Johnny) 1711,
Anthony (Tony) 1713,
Moses Sr. 1717, and
Joseph (Joe) 1720.

I was born in 1713, about 26 years prior to the dates when I first began to patent land.

I asked my father, John Sr., "Where were we younger children raised?"

"Tony, from the time of your tenth birthday you lived mostly with your grandfather on Bermuda and later, with me in Charleston.

Father John Sr. added, "When your brothers started getting involved with the pirates at Nassau your trips with them were declared off limits by your old granddad, Florentius (Flor) Cox.

"Flor had been a bit of a freebooter himself back in the old days but now was settled down on the family fifty acre plot on Bermuda from where he conducted a modest shipping business.

"When your brothers, John and Charles, started exploring the deep woods of North America for land, you and Moses were right behind them. As early as 1732, when you were but 19, you were assigned by the county fathers in Wilmington to help lay out a road, following in your brother Charles' footsteps."

Letter from Charles Cox

Joseph Cox
Charleston, South Carolina, 1739
Dear Youngest Brother,

I hear that Tony has patented 300 ac in Craven County.

Love from the deep woods,

Charlie

A Second Anthony Cox Journal Entry - 1745

Back In 1739 I happened to find out that Brother John was looking for land and had discovered some plots in Craven County, further north of Onslow and Carteret Counties, where John has spent much of his efforts. So John and I went upriver together, paddling a canoe against the current.

It was worthwhile; I patented two tracts, one in 1739 for 300 acres.

The land up north here is still plenty wild and there are nearly no settlers yet. So, while the choice of land is very good the security is bad. There are still many Indians in the area and it wouldn't do to patent land on which an Indian tribe has a village.

The Indians still do not accept the idea that a single man can own a piece of property and have sole use of it. The idea of trespass is foreign to them. Thus one must be careful when trying to keep Indians off one's property or one might find himself full of Indian arrows.

In 1743, John and I were talking as we paddled our canoes along the Neuse River. At first the well covered river bank yielded us no information. But the country had a warm climate, one that should be good for crops for a good part of the year.

John called out, "A village ahead on the right."

"I see it. Let's give it a try."

We coasted some and our little boats slowed to a

crawl. "Hello there," I shouted.

Soon some thirty Indians were converging on the river bank, women and children mostly, but a few adult men as well.

We were helped to mount our canoes onto the land next to the river. We got out and stretched and waited while several Indians ran back into the center of the village of teepees from where an Indian with three bright eagle feathers hanging from his head came out to us.

"Qui allez vous?" the Indian asked, speaking in French.

John answered using sign language. "We come to trade. We need a place to pitch our tent. And we are looking for land, maybe 400 acres, where we might raise wheat or maize."

"How many you?"

"My family, me, my brother, my spouse and three children."

"Why do you need so much land?"

"Maybe we can raise wheat to eat and to trade for other produce."

Now a big chief wearing a feathered hat entered the discussion. "You no need so many lands."

John said, "No, not now, maybe later."

The big chief said, "Here. We give you an arrow." He shot John in the thigh, once and then another time.

I was shocked. I moved toward John, to help him, I thought.

The chief notched another arrow. He looked at me and raised the bow and the arrow. "You want?"

I stopped still, "No," and I shook my head.

He motioned me back to my canoe. "You go."

"What of my brother?" I asked.
"Go. He will stay in our village."
Later we heard that John had been killed.

In 1745 I acquired another tract of 200 acres on the Neuse but I didn't stop to talk with the Indians about it.

We Cox brothers acquired other lands near Turkey Creek in Lower Onslow County in the 1740's.

When Cape Fear River land became available the three brothers migrating into North Carolina each patented 400 acre sections. Brother Joseph, living in Charleston, also acquired a patent on 400 acres on Cape Fear River, adjacent to Charles' plot.

[Ed. Joseph in his will c1761 left 300 acres of this Cape Fear River land to Charles Cox's son Moses Jr.]

Christmas 1746
Brothers Cox and sons,
Deep in the Woods of
North Carolina

Land on Cape Fear, Craven, Duplin Counties

Anthony Cox In the Records

1744 - Showed proof that I was entitled to 400 acres of property on the Cape Fear River, New Hanover County.-

1745 - Anthony Cox:
      - patent 180 ac Craven County
      - patent 180 ac Duplin County (adjacent to
        New Hanover on Cape Fear)

**1746 - I patented 400 ac on Cape Fear
      River, New Hanover County. [see 1744.]**
      - patent 180 ac Duplin County
1780 - Solomon patented 200 acres in Duplin
        County.

Joseph Cox
October 1752
Charleston, North Carolina

Dear Joe,

I accompanied Moses on one of our tours as members of the militia. We were garrisoning the British post at Pickwillany over the mountains in western Virginia when we were ambushed by an Indian war party. I managed to kill two of the warriors as we made our way off through the woods. We were chased by the war party but managed to keep ahead of the Indians. They tracked us day and night and as the Indians are very good at this sort of thing we were constantly expecting another attack.

    I expect to return to Charleston soon.

signed: Tony

A Anthoney Journal Entry - At Charleston

Moses has a Major Mallone, the garrison commander here at the fort in Charleston, with whom he
works. When the Major needs more militia for a
journey against the French or the Indians he con-
tacts Moses and Moses then passes the word and
gets us plenty of colonial recruits. Now with the
woods becoming more dangerous it ain't no trouble
for Moses to bring in a pile of wild mountain men
from the west or pull a group from right here near
town.

One time I was standing next to Big Al, a fellow
member of the militia, and we were getting washed
up a bit before having a bite of grub. Out of the
woods came a heavily weighted arrow and it drove
right into Big Al's back some six inches to a foot or
more. I'd never seen an arrow so big.

I looked around for the warrior that used the bow
as I expected he would be planning to send an arrow
after me.

I thought I saw the ground foliage flutter and I let
go with a bullet from my rifle but my shot did not
appear to find its target as there was no yell. I knelt
down and tended to big Al, my mate at the wash
stand. I got him out of there and helped clean his
wound. Believe me, pushing and pulling a big arrow
out of a wound is no picnic. We had blood spouting

all over for awhile and Al was swearing at us all.

From the woods,

Tony

Craven County Taxpayers, on Neuse River

1739 - Anthony Cox - 300 acres
1745 -   - 180 acres
1754 - Edward Cox in militia for Craven County,
        Newbern Dist. along with John Cox,
        Elisha, Elisha Jr., John Starkey Jr. and
        William Cox.
1769 - Thomas
1769 - Longfield Cox
1769 - Joseph
1769 - Edward
1769 - Harmon
1769 - Thomas, son of John
1769 - Thomas Jr.

Anthony's last official record was his acquisition of
land in 1745. He is assumed to have been killed by
Indians on his land in Craven County.

BOOK THREE - SECOND GENERATION

TWENTY

WITH JOHN ADAMS in BOSTON

A Moses Cox Jr. Journal Entry

I was born in Onslow County in about 1743, the third son of Charles Cox and Rebecca. My father was a part time pirate and my mother had been abducted by my father as part of his plunder when capturing a Spanish vessel.

But by the time I was born, Father Charles had given up his old ways and was now a hunter, fisherman, planter and farmer, the proud holder of several sites in New Hanover and Onslow Counties. Father owned land and a small cabin in a location called Indian Grove, near the Cape Fear River.

Father Charles said, "The land was of only mar-

ginal quality and so I continued looking for land until I found a richer plot of land with deep black soil.
It was located up in northern Onslow County."

While I was yet a teen age son I became enamored
with British politics. I understood that in 1756 William Pitt became British Prime Minister. He was involved in a war with France. In North Carolina we
called this war the **French and Indian War**. We
colonists had to watch out for the French soldiers,
the French settlers and the Indians who were allied
with the French.

I asked my dad, "Father, you and my uncles all
wanted the English to send troops to chase the
French and Indians away from our part of the country."

Father Charles said, "Old Pitt, he says he's going
to take the war to the enemy. The French have many
outposts on the other side of the mountains and
when me and my brothers go over there in search of
pelts the Indians attack us and chase our folks back
to the sea coast. Mr. Pitt sent some troops over to
help us out but then he said that we'd have to help
out too.

"We were all in militia units anyway so we allowed
we'd try to help ourselves when the time came."

When I turned 17, Mother Rebecca finally allowed
me to leave home, and in 1760 to join the Charleston
marine militia.

Our family still had two sloops left over from my
grandfather John's time as a mariner Captain. One,
which we called our war sloop, the *Wild Rover*, was
big enough to carry six cannons. I took some of the

militia and joined the British in fighting the Spanish
on the high seas. Then I joined up with the British
Navy when they got into several battles against the
French in Canada. It's so cold up there in Canada
that even the polar bears can't stand the cold. They
build houses out of the ice and hide in them all winter long.

In the Records

1761 - Moses Cox Jr. (18 years old) test for Lewis
Williams sale on S.W. branch of New River.

1761 - Given 400 acres on Cape Fear River by my
father, next to land of Joseph Cox.

1761 - Moses Cox Jr. and Hannah Williams married. Merge

1762 - Hannah and Moses Cox Jr. test (Hannah
Williams).

1767 - **Moses Cox Jr.** (b. c1743) and Jasper, sons
of Charles, (b. c1709) test.

1767/9 - Moses Cox, Jr. (b. c1743), and Hannah
(Williams) Cox (his wife), and Jasper Cox
(b. 1742), his brother, tests on a docu
ment in Onslow County.

1769 - Moses Cox Jr. pays taxes in Onslow
County.

1771 - Tax list - Onslow County - Charles Cox Sr.,
and sons Aaron, Charles Jr. & Moses Jr.

1772 - Moses Cox Jr. and Aaron Cox (sons of
Charles Sr. b. c1709), executors of estate of
Charles Cox Sr., (b. c1709, d 1771).

1773 - Virginia radicals begin rousing the populace against Great Britain.

Moses Cox Jr's Will (c1743 - 1775)

1775 - will - Moses Cox (b. c1743) to wife, Elizabeth (sister of John Foyle), and daughters, Henrietta, Matilda, Hannah and Celeia and sons Williams, Eli and Josiah, Onslow County.

> First wife was Hannah Williams.
> Witness was Willoughby Shackleford.
> **Matilda Cox** married Lott Ballard
> **Josiah Cox** married Margaret Shackleford, only daughter of William.

1775 - **Moses Cox, Jr**. 2nd N.C. during the American Revolution along with brothers Aaron and Charles and cousins Andrew and Solomon, sons of Moses Sr. and John, son of John. etc..relatives.

1776 - The Southern Campaign by the English to capture Charleston. Battle of Moore's Creek Bridge, N.C. Moses Jr. killed in action. Brought home to Richlands for burial.

1778 - Sold from Moses Cox Jr's estate, land 200 acres for 210 pounds on N.W. branch of New River. Elizabeth, Moses' 2nd wife and widow, to enjoy the property for lifetime. Test John Boston.

JASPER (JESSE) COX

Some Jasper (Jesse) Journal Entries

I'm the youngest of Charles Cox's four sons, born in 1747 four years after Moses Jr. in the area of Onslow County known as Richlands, because of the fantastic soil we had and the depth of our black dirt.

I had a wonderful time growing up as I had three older brothers to teach me the ways of the forest in which we lived, great land on which to hunt for deer, turkeys and rabbits.

John told me, "It's all right to track deer but only till you find their tracks. Then it's best to find a place to hide such that you can see the animal as it approaches. This is especially good if there is snow of course. Trouble is that with soft snow and a comfortable sitting position hidden in the trees there's a propensity to fall asleep. I've awakened suddenly, only to see a deer just going out of my range. Several times, I've found deer tracks within five feet of where I had fallen asleep in a gentle snow storm."

I asked Charles about the river on our land.

Charles said, "Yep, we have a river passing right

through our property. The fish are so thick that one can walk across without touching the water, like a god."

I asked, "You mean we can walk on the water?"

He grinned at me, "No we walk on the fish!"

Being the youngest boy I was spoiled by my three sisters too. They took pleasure at making me learn how to read and to write with a neat hand. My brothers had me write all their letters for them. I got so I could manufacture the best love letter in our part of the Carolinas. All the girls who thought they loved my brothers because of the love letters they received from them really loved me. I composed them all.

But my ability did me no good as my own love left me and moved over the mountains to Tennessee with her family when I was only twelve. We wrote one another.

One year she wrote, "I'm sorry Jesse, but a brave hunter has come our way. He has asked me to join him and I've agreed. I must give you up as a lost cause. He and I are moving on to Texas."

In 1763 I met my Uncle Moses at the patent office in Charleston and signed on for a big section of land on the Cape Fear River in New Hanover County. It was 640 acres at a spot that joined the low ground and the river. It seems to have been near the land earlier patented by Uncles Joseph and Charles in 1743.

I began working my new land as a large farm which had as yet to be cleared. So I spend much of my time in downing trees and hauling the trunks away to the river.

From 1767 on Moses Jr. and I did most of the attesting on contracts, etc., for the family (see earlier entries in this chapter).

I was on the tax roll in Onslow County for 1769."

Jasper Works for John Adams in Boston

There was a big fight up in Boston in 1770, the **Boston Massacre**. Big numbers of men were killed on both the British and the colonists side. So I left the homestead and wandered up that-a-way.

I read in the local Boston paper that Mr. Adams was looking for someone to transcribe his notes. So I interviewed with him and signed up with Mr. John Adams for room and board.

"Thank you Jasper. I can well use your handwriting skills as I write a great many letters."

I stayed with Mr. Adams for several years, doubling my pay and getting a bonus.

Mr. Adams was certainly a revolutionary. I'm surprised that the British did not take him prisoner or shoot him.

In 1773 the English parliament passed the Stamp Act and the following year tea came into Boston Harbor with a duty attached to it. Some of we more radical revolutionaries got together one night and dumped a big portion of the cargo into Boston Harbor. We dressed like Indians but the British were not fooled.

The British parliament passed a bill closing Boston Harbor. Further there were other laws setting aside then existing forms of government. Ben Franklin was dismissed as the American postmaster and Governor Hutchinson was replaced by General Gage. The bad laws were enforced.

Now the folks in Suffolk County worked up a plan for resistance. They put in their own revolutionary government.

In May 1774 Virginia elected delegates to a Continental Congress and other colonies followed suit.

Mr. John Adams attended as a representative from Massachusetts. I went along to help him with his letters home to Abigail (his wife). He wrote that the delegates were entertained in Philadelphia with sinful feasts. Adams found them to be great! He wrote that they were illustrative that the attendees were more than just radicals.

A second congress was called for in 1775.

I left Mr. Adams at this point and went home to help my family defend the old homestead against the British and the marauding Tories.

After I left, the situation got worse in Boston Town. The British began throwing around their power and some battles occurred at Lexington and Concord, Massachusetts. Within a year General Gage and Howe along with a thousand Tories had retired from Boston.

Back home in North Carolina I joined the militia in

fighting delaying actions against the Tories being recruited by General Clinton.

In January 1776, Tom Paine published a pamphlet called **Common Sense**. This pamphlet spelled out the reasons why America should be a free and separate nation separate from England. While many of our men could not read they got the gist of the content through a series of readers like me, reading a portion at a time.

In late February 1776 the British had rounded up a bunch or Tories and provided them with firearms. These men were marching from upland North Carolina to join the British forces at Wilmington when our forces intercepted them. We crushed all 1600 of them.

The British troops and ships attacked Charleston in June 1776 but they were driven off by the Carolina militia.

After over a year of fighting the British were not in control of any major section of the colonies. The average American was feeling more and more like an American, no longer a British subject.

Aaron and Sons Have a Discussion, Jasper narrates.

One day in late 1776 after the Declaration of Independence was published, my brother, Aaron and I, along with some of the other sons of Aaron, were discussing politics.

I said, "I don't believe in inheritance."

Aaron said, "Jasper, you mean like in England where the King and royalty leave their titles to their children?"

I said, "We shouldn't do that in America."

Aaron clarified, "You mean that Charles Sr. should not have left his patented and worked land to his children and they to the grandchildren?"

"Yes."

"Then nobody would own any land from their parents."

"Right."

"But Jasper, how would they get land so they could raise crops and cattle and children?"

I said, "They can get jobs working for someone and when they got enough money they'd place a down payment on some land."

"What would happen to the father's land, say like Charles' 640 acres?"

I said, "I don't know. Maybe it would go back to the State of North Carolina. The State could give it to someone else to patent. Charles sons, like you Aaron, might try to patent it, or some part of it."

Charles Cox Jr. said, "Our father gave some of us land before he died. What of that?"

I said, "He couldn't do that. All land would revert back to the state."

Charles Jr. said, "That's no good. One man works hard and he can't give away or leave any possession greater than someone who does nothing?"

I said, "But he could live a more pleasant life, spending everything he has and not bothering with accumulating property."

Aaron said, "But that goes against everything democratic and free. Here in America men need to

be free to have, gain and dispose of property as they
see fit. The Indians don't believe in holding property, but even they pass down the things that they
have owned, their ponies, their wigwam, their right
to vote in council. They especially pass on their ability to think, to talk with the Great Spirit, and their
ability to ride horses and to climb trees, mountains
and structures."

I said, "What of the fellow who comes to America
with a bundle of his father's money and steps in and
buys up the rights to ten thousand acres? I can't see
why he should have more land or power in America
than me, whose father left him very little."

"But that was your father's decision. He knew
that you already had more land than he did what
with that 400 acres you patented on the Cape Fear."

I said, "And why do I do better than some others
who don't patent any land?"

"That goes back to the Declaration...you are free,
you have the same inalienable rights as I do, and you
can pursue happiness just as I do. Sure, you do better if your family can provide you with some things
first so you don't have to develop them perhaps. But
that includes the mind that you got, fifty percent
from mother and fifty percent from father. or perhaps that's twenty five percent from each grandpar-
ent. It also includes how much drive you have, what
forcefulness, what ability to relate or adapt to your
environment, whatever it is."

I said, "You're saying there are some parts of anybody's inheritance that one can't keep from
taking...brain, some personality, and the things that
make us unequal in spite of what the Declaration
has to say and who has what land or money."

Aaron, "That's right. And personally I prefer being unequal with respect to my brain and my heart
than I do about 40, 80 or 640 acres of land. I'd
gladly give some King or wealthy person my land in
return for my own brain and my own children rather
than his. My children and grandchildren have a head
start over most any other children, however well en-
dowed with riches, because they are my descendants."

TWENTY ONE

CAPTURED by the TUSCARORA INDIANS

A Charles Cox Jr. Journal Entry

I am **Charles Cox Jr.** born in 1738 to Charles (b. 1709) and Rebecca Cox. They had four boys; **Charles Jr.** (me), Aaron, Jasper, and Moses, Jr. This Moses Jr. designation was used to differentiate Charles' son, Moses, from Charles' brother Moses. They had two girls; Susannah and Sarah.

Aaron and I and our older sister, Susannah, were born in Charleston, South Carolina and the other three children in the woods of eastern North Carolina, near an area called Richlands, on the N. W. Branch of New River. We are part of an extended family of cousins made up of three from Uncle John, two from Uncle Moses, six from Uncle Joseph and two from Uncle Anthony.

Jasper had no children. Uncle Joseph lived in

town with his children; Uncle John lived near us in
Onslow County; Uncle Moses near by on the Cape
Fear River; while Uncle Anthony spent most of his
time off in the woods with the militia chasing Indians and fighting the French on the frontier.

In the spring of 1742 my father brought my siblings
to the deep woods where he and Mother Rebecca,
had set up a small log cabin.

In 1743 Father Charles and Uncle Jasper spent
the entire spring and summer chopping down trees
and enlarging a new cabin to accommodate a separate eating room, a sleeping room for my father and
mother, and two second story rooms for we children
to sleep in, total four rooms. This was built on the
newly acquired land in Richlands.

Jasper, when staying with us, got to sleep by himself in the main room; that used for cooking and eating.

Jasper and my father also added on a pantry for
keeping supplies, storing salted meat, etc. My
mother, in the meantime, developed a garden for
vegetables, plants for seasoning, and special places
for raising flowers for the table. And they built several out buildings, a food and hurricane cellar, a
barn and an outdoor kitchen. When all was done, father gave his brother Jasper his acquired land on the
Cape Fear near where Uncles John and Joseph had
patented land.

When I was five, my mother began teaching me
the alphabet and some words. As the years progressed in the deep woods, where there were no
schools, mother taught my brothers and sisters to
read and write and work with numbers. Father

Charles could do numbers but he had to rely on mother for reading our letters and for answering his brothers' correspondence.

Jasper's Story About Being Captured by Indians

In 1755 Aaron and I were captured by a wandering band of Indians while we were traveling in the forest, coming home from Uncle Anthony's home where we'd been visiting Cousins John and Elisha in Craven County, upriver from our land in Onslow County. The woods were growing very tightly together so we had taken a canoe up the river, thinking to float back downstream.

After leaving John and Elisha, Uncle Anthony's boys, we were moving back downstream at a pretty good speed when suddenly the river was blocked by several Indian canoes filled with Tuscarora Indians from a fearful tribe residing to the north of us. Taking alarm, Aaron and I tried to drive our heavily loaded canoe between two of the Indian canoes, but several Indians jumped into the water and grabbed hold of the gunwales of our small vessel. Other Indians placed arrows into position on their bows and made as though to fire them at us.

Aaron made a gesture to stop them and held up his hands empty of any weapon.

We were handled roughly, but not such as to give us serious injuries. Our arms were tied and we were urged to go where the Indians pointed, back up the river and off on another smaller tributary to the East. Any hopes that Elisha or John might see us was lost when the Indians cached their canoes (and

ours) and concealed them with the branches of surrounding trees. We headed into a thin strand of trees
toward the East.

The Indians did not blindfold us, but merely
prodded us when we did not keep up to these well
conditioned men. They were perhaps twenty years
old and appeared to be a hunting party rather than a
war party.

Aaron looking at the Indians addressed me, "We
better not resist. These warriors are young. They
might try anything to gain recognition."

I tried to respond to Aaron, and started, "Aaron I
would..."but one of the Indians hit me with the handle part of his hatchet. I shut up.

In due time we arrived at an Indian encampment. It
was on another river, a long fast walk east of New
River. I whispered to Aaron, "I think this is perhaps
the Neuse River."

Aaron answered, "Yes, it seems to be parallel."

An Indian prodded him and shut him up.

Finally the Indians released us from our bonds but
gave us to understand we were not to go anywhere.
Young Indian boys and girls came and ran around
and threw objects at us. Occasionally a bigger boy
would throw a rock at us. The Indian women stood
around us in a circle. They seemed to be telling the
boys to stop throwing the rocks.

The braves were obviously discussing something
about us. "Aaron," I said, "Those fellows are discussing whether to kill us."

"How do you know this?"

"Some of the braves make a remark to the other braves and then point a finger at us."

Finally something was decided and three of the Indians looking rather disgusted at the whole thing came over to us.

One pointed to me, "You."

"Me?"

"Take off your clothes."

"No."

"Take them off." He prodded me with a spear.

I took off my shirt and handed it to him.

He took the shirt and handed it to one of the boys.

"Take off pants." He prodded me with the spear again.

I took off the deerskin trousers. He took them and gave them to an Indian boy with about my waist size. "Here," he said in Indian language, "put these on."

He looked at me, in a pair of shorts, "Off," he said. He pointed his bow at my shorts.

I took them off and stood there in my pure pale skin, all showing, from head to ankle.

The Indian squaws giggled and so did the girls.

The Indian looked at my moccasins. "Off."

I took them off and left them on the ground. I was now naked to the tip of my toes.

The Indian looked at Aaron, "You." He made a motion with the bow.

Aaron got undressed.

The Indian split up all of our clothes to the Indian

boys who tried some on and traded some with the other recipients of our clothes.

I was chilly now and began to shiver a little. I said to the Indian, "Its frigid, cold. We need clothes."

"No. No clothes. Sit near fire or go wigwam." He made a motion to one of the tents.

We stayed in the village for three days and then were assigned to a small group of five Indian braves going out into the woods. We were given our moccasins but not any clothes.

"You come with us," one of the braves with three feathers tied to his hair piece said. From then on I called him, Three Feathers.

We were given a load of food and spare weapons, arrows, to carry, packaged as a load which could be carried on our backs.

Off they went. The Indians moved through the woods rather fast, dodging tree trunks and branches with ease. Aaron and I kept getting hit by the branches and it was obvious that we were not so agile as the Indians. But the Indians did not slow down for us, rather prodding us with their spears, until we had bruises all about our posteriors.

After an uncertain distance we came to a river, one which I thought might be New River, as we had been traveling southward. There, the Indians stopped for supper. Two Indians left us then, one going up and other down stream.

In the morning our back packs were opened and the contents were used for breakfast. What was left was divided among the five Indians.

Three Feathers said, "We let you go now. See, there in the river is your canoe, floating down stream toward the big water."

With that, the Indians all faded back into the trees leaving us naked in the woods with our canoe out in the middle of the river and floating high in the water. The two of us could both swim so we started down stream along a path along the water until we got some distance ahead of the canoe. Then we dived into the river and swam out to the canoe. We were so exhausted by the time we got to the canoe that we were almost unable to climb aboard. But get aboard we did. The paddles were gone.

We floated on down stream until I was able to catch hold of an overhead branch and pull us to shore.

Much later we were able to bring our little vessel and its two passengers into shore at our father's farm in upper Onslow County. We were an exhausted pair of naked woodsmen, dragging into camp, before our extended family. Embarrassment was hardly a strong enough word to express our feelings.

Signed...Jasper Cox

Charles Cox Jr. Journal entry of September, 1765

1765 - I read in the Charleston paper that old Ben Franklin is at it again with the British. Recently he tried to write their laws with respect to the colonies, saying the British should be partial toward us because what we do is good for the empire. Putting penalties on us via taxation is no help at all and may lead to a desire for independence.

Down here in North Carolina we don't have much contact with the British except for to pay taxes.

Charles Cox Jr.

In the Records

1770 - Sale to **Charles Cox, Jr.** 170 acres on NW branch of New River at Felix Kenon's corner. Test Moses Cox, Jr. and John Boston.

1771 - Tax list - Onslow County - **Aaron, Charles Jr., Moses Jr.**

1776-1781 - **Moses Cox,** Jr. 2nd N.C. during Am Revolution per "Land Grants and pay vouchers re. American Revolution"..along with brothers **Aaron** and **Charles Cox, Jr.** and cousins **Andrew** and **Solomon,** sons of Moses Sr. and **John,** son of John. etc...brothers and cousins.

Charles Cox Jr. a member of the militia for Wilmington District (Onslow County) along with **Solomon** Cox, **Simon** Cox and **Aaron** Cox (b. 1741).

1780 - Jurors in Onslow County: Charles Cox, Jr., Stephen Shackleford, Jonathon Wilder, Aaron Cox, William Hawkins, Benjamin Williams, (3) Wards, etc.

1792 - Sale of land by **Charles Cox, Jr.,** John Cox's line. Test Aaron Cox Sr., Jesse Cox Sr. Signed by **Charles III and Hannah Cox.** (children of

Aaron Cox Sr.)

1795 - **Moses** and **Stephen Cox, sons of Charles Jr. are orphans**.

1796 - Stephen and Moses test on the sale of land.

[Ed. Charles Jr. had five boys who divided up the estate. The boys were:

    # 1. - Charles IV, (b. c1768), named for father.

    # 2.- Moses III - (b. c1775), named for Moses Jr.

    # 3. - Stephen Jr, - (b, c1775).

    # 4. -Eli - (b. c1771), mother's side.

    # 5. - Asa - (b. c1774), mother's side.]

1807 - Benjamin Barranau sold 103 acres near Little N.W. of Little River to Charles Cox IV for 190 pounds.

Division of Charles Cox, Jr.'s Property

1807 - Charles Cox IV (b. c1768) (son of Charles Jr. (b. c1738) who was the son of Charles Sr. (b. c1709)) sold to Cader Cox land at Cox's Swamp which is part of the land of Charles Cox Jr. (b. 1738, recently deceased) which fell to Charles Cox Jr. at the death of Charles Sr. eg, about 56 acres. [Note. a Charles III was the son of Aaron, about the same age as Charles IV.]

1807 - Moses Cox III (b. 1775), son of Charles Cox Jr. (b. c1738), grandson of Charles Cox, Sr. (b. c1709) sold to Cader Cox (b. c1775), son of Aaron, (b. c1741) 56 1/4 acres, his share of court order. Aaron Cox Sr., Stephen Cox, (b. c1775) (Moses' brother) test.

1807 - Moses Cox III (b c1775), son of Charles
Cox Jr. sold to Hardy Cox 16 2/3 acres, his share of
50 acres granted in 1782 and 29 1/3 acres his part of
the dowry of Hannah Cox, widow of Charles Cox Jr.
(b. c1738).

1810 - Eli and Asa, (b. c1771 & 1774), sons of
Charles Cox Jr. sold property as heirs of estate of
Hannah Cox, widow of Charles Cox, Jr.

1810 - Asa Cox, son of Charles Cox Jr., of State
of Georgia, sold property in Onslow County, North
Carolina.

1810 - Francis Humphrey sold 50 acres to Charles
Cox IV (at Charles Cox's line.)

1810 - Stephen Cox sold 68 1/4 acres on Cox's
Swamp for 162 pounds re court order to Charles IV,
Moses III, and Stephen Cox (himself), three of the
five children of Charles Cox Jr.. Says he is Hannah's
son-in-law.   [Ed. This Stephen probably went to
Florida with William Cox in 1824 - 1825. Seems to
be in same age bracket as Hardy, Cader and Aaron
Jr.]

Where They Went

Stephen (b. 1775) went to Florida with William
Cox (b. 1796) in 1824.

Asa (b. 1774) went to Georgia with Hardy Cox Jr.
and Eli Cox (son of Aaron)

Moses III (b. 1780), son of Chas Jr., may have
gone to Florida.

Charles IV (b. 1770), son of Charles Jr.

Eli Jr. (b. 1775), named after Uncle Eli.

TWENTY TWO

AARON and BENEDICT ARNOLD

An Aaron Journal Entry

I, Aaron Cox, was born in 1741, the second eldest of the four boys sired by Charles Sr. See chapter 21 for all their names.

During my growing up period my family lived on the original 640 acre of land patented by my father, Charles Cox Sr. in 1741. I never did have a pair of shoes until I went off to serve with the militia during the revolution.

I, Uncle Moses who had served with Colonel Washington during the war against the French and Indians, and my cousins Solomon and Andrew went up north to New England in 1777 to help him out against the Red Coats.

We got hooked up with one of Washington's generals named Lee. He was in charge of half of Washington's troops and was stationed at the main garrison in New York. We got assignments as aides. I was assigned to help write and rewrite his communica-

tions to the various commanders under him and to
Washington. Lee's letters were not so friendly to
Washington as I would expect.

General Lee had a friend on Washington's staff in
New Jersey. He was a general named Reed who had
written to my boss saying, "We here under George
Washington are about to flee from this garrison at
Fort Washington. We have found out that a strong
British column is approaching. This has frightened
General Washington. If you hurry here you could
demonstrate what Washington hasn't done. You
could save the army from incompetent command."

I couldn't believe the note from Reed, as I opened
it as part of my aide duties for General Lee.

I took the memo to General Lee. I said, "Looks
like Washington's running from the British."

"You accustomed to opening other peoples'
mail?"

"That's part of my job, sir."

"Is it part of your job to blab about it?"

"No sir," I said.

A week later we got a letter from Washington telling
us about the escape he and his troops had experienced. He asked General Lee, "Bring your troops
over from New York to New Jersey so the combined
force can defend New Jersey from the British."

He wrote, "I have to put up some defense or else
the people of New Jersey might go over to the British and become Torys."

In the same pouch I found another letter from
General Reed. He said, "The entire army feels that
Lee's presence was needed. You are our only hope."

We heard that Washington was falling back before a strong British force. Then I hand carried to General Lee another Reed message saying that there was too much opportunity for Lee in New York and that Lee should not come to New Jersey."

When the mail pouch went out I incorrectly addressed the response to Reed, sending it instead direct to General George Washington. Soon both generals realized that Washington was aware of their measurement of his worth as a general (poor).

Finally my general decided to obey orders. He took our force into New Jersey. Washington wrote telling General Lee to proceed with an attack against the British. Lee who was a great ladies man proceeded with the attack but first he had a date with the pretty barkeeper of an inn nearby his army.

At his headquarters we got word that the general had been taken prisoner by the British who had found him in bed at the inn with the barkeep.

Washington summoned all of Lee's troops to join him in Pennsylvania.

General Howe, the British leader in New York, now believed that all the civilians in New Jersey were going over to the British side, having been deserted by Washington. Howe therefore decided to place military posts throughout New Jersey as a sign of the pacification of the area.

He left a two to three thousand Hessian force at Trenton where they rested and waited for Christmas.

#

Trenton, Christmas 1777

Washington decided to use some Indian warfare tactics on against the waiting British forces. He would cross the Delaware at three points and catch the Hessians by surprise and surround them. He would do this on Christmas day. It started to snow at around midnight. Some of our forces demobilized and returned to their tents.

The rest of us were mobilized and sent out on small boats to cross the Delaware River opposite the City of Princeston. Washington stood up in his boat nearly causing it to capsize in the major snow storm which seemed to block our way.

The ice in the river forecast a dreadful return voyage. It grew colder and colder, such that ice formed on our beards and ears. Soon we couldn't recognize our own uniforms. The snow turned to hail and daylight appeared in the eastern sky. It was to be a typical hellish winter day in New Jersey.

The battle at Trenton was one of astonishment in that the Hessians were caught completely by surprise. They were awakened in their barracks, unable to see in the snow storm, and unable to form ranks for defense. The surrender came after but a short time. We Americans had no losses at all.

The way back was indeed terrible but now the Americans brought with them over nine hundred Hessian prisoners, six brass cannons, piles of arms and wagons filled with supplies.

Washington's troops scored a great victory over the English. I was so excited that I went and enlisted with the Wilmington District militia for the duration of the war.

When I came back from New Jersey, Mary and I begun having a family of our own with a half dozen boys and at least three girls. I never made up a will, just not planning to die while I was only 66 years of age (1807 - 1741 = 66).

#

In the Records

1769 / 70 - Aaron Cox, tax list, Onslow County.
     In N.C. militia, no. 3560, 2nd Regiment,
     N. C., Wilm Dist. Tax list - Craven Cty.

1769 - Charles Jr., tax list, Onslow.
     In N.C. militia, 2nd and 3rd Wilm Dist.

1769 -   Jesse or Jasper, taxes Onslow.,

1769 - Moses Jr., taxes Onslow.

1770 - Tax list - Onslow County - John Cox and Solomon Cox, sons of John, **Aaron Cox**, son of Charles Sr.

1771 - Moses Jr. 2nd N.C., militia.

1771 - Simon, Militia, Wilmington Dist.

1776-1781 - Aaron Cox, 2nd N.C. Militia, during Am Revolution. .**along with brothers Moses Cox Jr., and Charles Jr.** and cousins Andrew and Solomon, sons of Moses Sr. and John, son of John. etc...brothers and cousins.

1778 - Jasper Cox, First N.C., sick at Prince
     Town, 9/8/78, commanded by Col. Tho
     mas Clark. Enlist 19 June 1777, 3 years,

1779 - Jasper Cox, Sgt. 15 June.

1797 - Jasper Cox, 274 acres, 29 Nov. # 5010.

#

Aaron's Journal Continued re. Valley Forge

Along about February of '78 I got assigned by the Second North Carolina to General Washington's staff at Valley Forge, Pennsylvania. I was an aide or aide-de-camp because my handwriting was superior to anyone else in our unit. It seems the General was desperate to have his messages to congress and to his officers be legible. He'd been going through aides faster than a hound dog scratches off flees.

I was doing rather well until I started getting a wrist that hurt like a series of bumble bee stings. I didn't want to lose this job though as it was interesting watching the general and his staff at the job of running our American army. But General Washington; he was editing one of my letters to Benjamin Franklin one evening. He looked over at me sitting at a table near by.

General Washington asked, "You write this corporal?"

"Yes sir. I found it interesting."

"You're not supposed to read the letter."

"Sorry sir. But I have to understand it or I will write wrong things into the text."

"No matter. I can't read some of the words."

"I've a problem sir. My right wrist is in pain."

"Then use the other wrist."

"That's why you can't read the letter."

"A...hum."

He looked over to another aide, General Lafayette, "Mark," he asked, "Can't we get this corporal assigned elsewhere while his wrist heals up?"

"Can he dance?"

The general looked nonpulsed, "You dance?"

"I do a mean square dance and Virginia reel."

"That do Mark?"

"Better than most. General Arnold is looking for someone he can boss around and still take with him to the dances in Philadelphia."

"Dances is it?"

"Yes sir."

"Corporal Cox, it's to Philadelphia with ye. Report back here when the wrist is healed enough so you can transcribe letters for me again."

"Yes sir."

Aaron at Philadelphia

In July 1778 I reported to General Arnold at the military headquarters in Philadelphia. The British had evacuated Philadelphia and the Americans were once more in command here.

It was most interesting being in a large city during war time. Mostly our troops had been losing battles with the British but somehow our new country and its soldiers were still very much involved.

I was very much depressed at the situation here though. The city was going on much as it would have without a war. There was much in the way of commerce and ladies were on the streets all dressed in finery. And there were parties all about. My duties with the general as an aide were mostly needed in the evenings. I reported to him dressed in full dress uniform at seven pm and stayed on duty then until relieved. I attended parties with him, ran errands, and provided him with a partner when he was entertaining or having a late dinner with more than one lady friend at a time. It wasn't long before my rusty and back woods style of dancing had improved such that my partners and I often were called on to lead grand marches and to dance the first dance in that the general was still recovering from his wounds in combat.

Both the general and I were revelrous in a society higher than either of us had ever known.

The general soon became fascinated by high-born Peggy Shippen who had stayed in the city while it was occupied by the British. She had flirted with the British adjutant general, Major Andre, and was reputed to be a Tory. To impress Miss Peggy General Arnold was soon living and partying on a level that suggested that he was getting funds from a source other than his American army pay, perhaps graft.

I thought that things were a bit awry so I wrote General Washington how it was.

Next thing I knew, the general had me recalled. I reported to him back at Valley Forge. I was dressed in my dress uniform and I looked far better than the general who had been out in the rain and had mud on his pants and blouse.

"Sergeant Cox reporting, sir."

"That's a pretty nice uniform you have there son."

"Yes sir."

"How did you get it?"

"Miss Peggy had her family tailor make it up for me."

"You had money to pay for it?"

"No sir. Mr. Andre, a friend of Miss Peggy, had placed a sum of money with the tailor and told him to take care of any of Miss Peggy's needs. She sent me to the tailor and I instructed him how to make me a dress uniform."

"You had time to do this?"

"General Arnold only had need of my services in the evening sir."

"Anything else?"

"Yes. I think the general is going to marry Miss Peggy. But I think Miss Peggy and the British adjutant are playing a game behind the general's back."

"All right sergeant. Report back to Philadelphia."

I was still with Arnold when the general actually married Peggy Shippen and Washington came down to Philadelphia to attend the wedding, a gala affair in the City.

As time progressed, Peggy placed pressure on Benedict Arnold to earn more money and to attain a position of some high level in society. Peggy was pro-British now with no reservation and she provided a conduit between Arnold and Andre the British officer. Andre agreed to pay Arnold for intelligence and so a liaison began. [Ed. Andre asked Arnold to secure information about the American installation at West Point.]

I wrote General Washington of my fears but he never let on that he had any reason to mistrust Benedict Arnold.

Thus when Arnold seemed healed and could dance on high heels at the parties, Washington asked him if he were ready for a combat assignment.

Aaron and General Arnold at West Point

General Arnold said, "I would like to try my hand at managing a garrison, perhaps West Point."

Washington had not visualized placing this strong military fighter in such a static position. "I was thinking to make you commander of the whole right wing of the Continental Army."

Arnold then moped around headquarters and said, "I don't think I'm well enough for active service."

Washington pitied Arnold and thought that the wound had broken his spirit. But Arnold would talk of nought but West Point. Finally Washington gave him the position of Commander of West Point.

Two months later Washington, Lafayette, and Hamilton, while returning from his depressing interview with the French Leader, stopped to have breakfast with Arnold at his residence some miles from West Point where Washington was going to conduct an inspection. .

I met him at the entrance, "The general is not here, sir."

"I was to meet him."

"Yes, I am to serve you all breakfast and then take you on the river to the fortress where he is arranging a reception for you."

So Washington and his staff ate, then left, with me as a guide, for the fortress.

The fortress rose high above the river but there was no sign of a reception committee.

When Washington landed he asked for General Arnold, but the soldiers had not seen any sight of him. So Washington went ahead with a planned inspection.

Washington was getting spruced up for four o'clock dinner when news came that Peggy was indisposed and would not be there for dinner. A packet of papers was delivered to him as those just then taken from John Anderson, a spy. They contained letters from Arnold giving the British information that would help them in capturing West Point. The spy was the self same Major John Andre that had been associated with Peggy Shippen.

Washington was vivid with emotion and rage. "Whom can we trust now?"

Washington took Hamilton and myself by the arms. "You two, race to King's Ferry and see if you can stop Arnold from escaping to the British."

But we could not catch him and Arnold escaped to a British warship. He had sent General Washington letters trying to explain his reasons for treason. We took these back to Washington. But of course these only enraged Washington more.

Washington changed the guard at West Point to prepare for an assault from the river. During the night the wind changed. The British moved off.

Our army was now very short of supplies. Washington and his immediate staff was encouraging men to take leave or to shorten their time and to return to their home states to await for a need for soldiers when more funds might be available. I left and returned to my militia unit in North

Carolina...keeping watch for a future need. I
planned that Mary and I would begin another child
and maybe get some good farming started for the
year. But then I was also concerned about what the
British were doing in the Carolinas.

#

More in the Record

1780 - Jurors in Onslow County: Charles Cox, Jr.,
Stephen Shackleford, John Wilder, **Aaron Cox,**
William Hawkins, Benjamin Williams, (3) Wards,
etc.

1780/90 - Aaron Cox Sr. children

1777 - Hardy, 1783 - Aaron Jr., 1785 - Jesse (or
Jasper)
1787 - John, 1782 - Eli, 1790 - Cader, 1780 - Charles III
daughters: Susannah, Sarah, Hannah

1793 - Land Grant **Aaron Cox Sr.**(b. c1739), 140
ac, Onslow County.
1797 - **Aaron Cox Sr.** sold land to Lawrence Jarman (son-in-law) 100 acres at Cox's and Brown's
corner. **Signed by Aaron and Mary Cox.** Test
Charles Cox. [Ed. We don't know Mary's maiden
name. But she has two great-grandchildren named

Starkey Cox so perhaps her name was Mary Starkey, daughter of John or Peter Starkey. More likely it was Mary Gregory, daughter of Hardy Gregory. This later would explain how Hardy Cox, one of Aarons and Marys first boys, got his name.]

#

Aaron Cox Journal Entry

Living on a farm, especially a big one of 640 acres makes for a hell of a life if you like the outdoors. Fortunately for me our part of the world had been pretty well organized by the time I had to fend for myself and my brood. We had good laws so that I didn't have to worry much about other men trying to take my property away from me. Actually I was able to patent more land. I don't have an awful lot left now that I am dying. I've been selling or giving chunks of land to my children.

So the family has a big problem in trying to divide my estate equally among my children and maintaining a dower right for Mary, my wife. But the work to split up everything (or to put it all together) should go pretty good I think. [We will see as we read the rest of this chapter].

LISTINGS OF AARON'S HEIRS

Division of Aaron's Property (1807 - 20)

1807 - Aaron Cox Sr., b. 1741, died in about 1807 at which point two of his elder sons, **Hardy** and **Eli**, began accumulating the rights to his land and Charles Cox Sr.'s land from the various children, grandchildren, and from Mary, Aaron's widow.

1808 - **Charles Cox III** and **Hardy Cox** (sons of Aaron) for 260 pounds, **deed to Eli** 100 acres of Aaron Cox Sr. (b. c1735) estate. Hardy in Onslow 1810 and 1820 censuses.

1809 - **Aaron Cox Jr.** (b c1770) sold to Eli Cox, son of Aaron Cox Sr, (b. c1735) his rights in his father's estate, Aaron Cox Sr. (b c1735), **16 acres**.

1810 - Aaron Cox Jr. and Eli Cox, sons of Aaron Sr., in Onslow census 104.

1810 - Charles Cox III, son of Aaron, in Onslow census.

The names of those with rights in Aaron's property

1815 - Eli Cox (b. 1786) (son of Aaron) acquired **rights** of land **in dower of Mary Cox**, widow of Aaron Sr. (b. c1735). Signed off by:
John Bailey,

Cader Cox (son of Aaron),

Charles Cox (son of Aaron), who married Sally Thompson,

William Tippett, who had married Susannah Cox,

Hardy Cox (son of Aaron) Sr.,

Hardy Cox Jr., (son of Jesse who was son of Aaron),

Susannah Tippett (daughter of Dorcas who was a daughter of Aaron),

Sukey Cox (daughter of Jesse who was son of Aaron)

(Nancy) Ann Bailey.

Hannah who married Benjamin Marshburn (Ed. Priscilla Cox witnessed her will in 1824). Marshburn named a son Hardy after Hannah's brother. This Hardy (Jr.) moved to Tennesee along with Eli, son of Aaron.

Aaron Jr. who married Elizabeth Gooding and went to Mississippi,

Dorcas who married Francis Humphrey,

Sally who married Risdon Barranau,

John,

Elizabeth who married Thomas Jarman, and

Rebecca.

From 1826 document re dowager rights sale to Eli

Susannah Cox who married Walter Tippit.

Hannah Cox

Eli Cox in Onslow 1810 and 1820 census

Nancy (or Ann) Cox who married John Baily

Charles Cox b. c1780, married Sally Thompson, 1820 census.

Hardy Cox who married the widow Priscilla Sweatman in 1797, b c1777, 1810 (26-45) and 1820 (26-45) census. May also have gone to Tennessee for the 1830 and 1840 census.

Jesse Cox who left two children as heirs, Hardy Jr. married in 1816 in Robison County, N.C. and Sukey who married John Glen(n).

Aaron Cox, Jr. in 1810 (26-45) (3 children) census, sold land in 1813 to go to Mississippi. Wife Elizabeth Gooding had land in Lenoir and Jones Counties.

Dorcas Cox m. Francis Humphrey.

Sally Cox.

Cader Cox in 1820 census, married Martha Thompson.

Sarah Cox married Risden Barranau.

Elizabeth Cox married Thomas Jarman.

Rebecca Cox (doc 1831 says she's an heir).

John Cox (doc 1831 says he's an heir).

#

TWENTY THREE

CAPE FEAR RIVER LAND

In the Records

1763 - Jasper (Jesse), (b. 1742) patented 640 acres (one square mile) on the N. E. Branch of Cape Fear River joining low ground and the river. Jesse (Jasper) was the brother of Aaron, (b. 1741) and the youngest son of Charles Cox Sr. (b. c1709).

The family had between 1500 and 2000 acres of land along the Cape Fear, all patented in the 1730's and 40's. When young Jesse had the chance to double the family's acreage in the area he leaped at the chance.

Wilmington

Wilmington, on the Cape Fear River, was one of the South's open-cities during much of the war. It was here where business as usual was carried on and

there was a level of social order. The planters put on
dances several times per month to which the soldiers
of the Carolina militia and the Continental Line
were invited, along with finely-dressed, local and
young, women and planter's wives.

For the women of the back country many whose
homes were accessible only by the rivers that made
their way back and forth from the ocean to the foot
hills of the western mountains, these dances were
"must" events. Here it was that Cox planter and farm
boys found members of the opposite sex dressed in
their wide swinging gowns with bare shoulders and
deep-open breasts.

The young patriotic men of the time were eager to
fight for their new country but the young women
were equally eager to comfort the young militia
member and to prepare for an ending of war and the
beginning of a new age to follow.

Joseph Cox's Land on Cape Fear River

1778 - To Moses Jr. (b. 1743) estate, son of
Charles Sr., 300 acres, for 30 pounds proclamation
money, part of greater acreage tract granted to Joseph Cox (b. 1720) in New Hanover County by patent dated 26 July 1743. Moses Jr. is a nephew of Joseph who is a brother of Charles Sr.. [Note: This is
from land originally in New Hanover but now it is in
Duplin County due to a change to the county
boundary lines.]

TWENTY FOUR

JOHN & SOLOMON, SONS OF JOHN Jr.

A John Cox III Journal Entry,

My brother, Solomon, and I were born in about
1735 and 1737 just before John Cox Jr., our father,
proved his rights to obtain 200 acres of land in Duplin County. He got 50 acres per person; having my
mother and we two boys besides himself. Our sister
was born in 1742 and then in 1743, our father, John
Jr., was killed by Indians as he and Uncle Charles
were negotiating for land.

This left my mother with three small children, me,
my brother and a sister to raise, and nothing but
some mostly undeveloped land in the Carolina
woods.

We moved back to Charleston where my mother
and we children moved in with my mother's parents,

on Church Street, not far from Uncle Isaac's.

Solomon and I joined our Uncle Joseph in the marine business, helping around the boat yard as our family built small vessels for use in trading along the coast. As we got older we also went to sea as able bodied seamen and as factors representing Joseph's business.

I also continued our family's interest in forest land and trading with the Indians.

When the war came along, both Solomon and I joined our militia and fought against the English.

Solomon was taken prisoner by a Tory unit of militia fighting on the English side. He was shot when trying to escape in 1775, even before the Declaration of Independence was published.

in the record

1769 - Hardy Gregory, Onslow County taxpayer.

1769 - Benjamin, Jesse Ballard, Onslow County taxpayers.

1770 - James, John Ballard, Onslow County taxpayer.

1770 - taxable: Onslow: **John and Solomon Cox** (b. c1738), sons of John Cox, New River, Hardy Gregory, Aaron Cox, son of Charles.

1771 - Hardy Gregory and John Gregory, tax list, Onslow County (cousins). Hardy Gregory was likely Aaron Cox's father-in-law.

1771 - John and Joseph Ballard, tax list, Onslow County.

1772 - Hopkin Wilder to John Wilder 140 acres. Test. Jonathan Wilder (son of Hopkin Wilder and grandfather of Sallie Shackleford who married William Cox and started the Florida clan of Coxes).

1772 - Moses Cox Jr., John Boston (married to a Cox girl) and **Jesse (Jasper)** Cox, test on sale of land on Jenkin's branch at Cox's corner.

1775-1781 - **"Land Grants and pay vouchers from American Revolution"**..Moses Cox Jr., 2nd N.C. during Am Revevolution along with brothers Aaron and Charles and cousins Andrew and Solomon, sons of Moses Sr., and **John, son of John Jr.** etc...brothers and cousins. [Think Moses Jr. prepared will in '75; died in the war.

1776-1783 - **List of Soldiers from North Carolina in the Am. Revolution [NCSAR]**

1775 - Solomon Cox, (b. 1737) son of John, killed; left all goods to brother John, (b. 1735), 40 years old.

1777 - John Cox of Dobbs County drafted into John Kennedy's Company. (7/6/77)

Aaron Cox, Jr. No. 3560, son of Aaron Sr. Wilmington Distr.in militia

Simon Cox, Wilmington Distr. in militia.

Solomon Cox, son of Moses Sr., Wilmington Distr. in militia.

Charles Cox, son of Aaron Sr., Wilminton Distr. in militia.

John Cox, son of Anthony, Newbern Distr, in militia. Also Elisha Cox, same as John.

Caleb and Joseph Cox, Hillsboro Distr, in militia.

John, Joseph and William Cox, Hillsboro Distr., Continential Line.

Andrew and Moses Cox, Capt Augustus Spain's Company, 2nd N. C. Regiment.

TWENTY FIVE

YORK TOWN 1775 - 1783

From the Records

May 30, 1775 - Josiah Martin, royal governor of N. C. locked the palace at New Bern and fled to Fort Johnson.

Knowing that there were many loyalists in the interior, Governor Martin had a plan where the British forces were to be sent directly from England to Cape Fear where they were to meet up with loyalists on February 5, 1776.

The Southern Campaign

[Ed. The Southern strategy was meant to enable the British to capture Cape Fear and thereby control the Southern colonies, block the use of the Whigs and enable mobilization of the Tories which were thought to outnumber the revolution oriented colonists.

The Tories did organize a force of 1600 which when armed with British weapons were thought to be superior to whatever the Patriots could bring against them.]

Andrew Cox Journal Entry

Our several militia units had been meeting twice a month for two years now so when word came to us that we were needed to stop a force of Tories coming from the west, we were all anxious to trot out with our hunting rifles and shot guns to meet these neighbors who sided with the British.

My brother Solomon joined me, "What do you think these Tories will be like?"

I said, "I suppose pretty much like us. I haven't figured out yet why one of us is for independence and the next is for continuing being English citizens."

Solomon said, "They say that the war has something to do with the way the world is changing."

"I suppose."

Solomon offered, "Some of us want to live in a welfare State and others want to live in a free merchandising state."

"I don't care one way or the other. I just want to be left alone in the woods or on my own farm."

Moore's Creek Bridge

At another time, Solomon asked me, "Andy, we going up by **Moore's Creek?**"

"That's what I hear."

"How soon?"

"As soon as we can make it, I suppose."

So we joined a small force of Patriots near **Moore's Creek Bridge** on February 25, 1776. By the 27th we numbered 1100. Both sides avoided head on battles and we finally stopped fighting when the Tories broke off and decided the bridge wasn't worth the losses they were experiencing.

Solomon asked me, "How come the British moved back?"

"I expect that the Tory forces that General Clinton, the British General, was hopeful for, didn't materialize."

"Maybe they didn't want to kill any of us."

"Yes. It's pretty hard to shoot at a fellow Carolinian when he ain't done you no wrong."

Solomon said, "I expect we get to go home now."

"How do you figure?"

"Well, there's no one to fight."

"Makes sense. But war time doesn't exist on sense."

Solomon questioned me, "So?"

"The British have a fleet coming on to Wilmington I hear."

"So?"

"Maybe we'll have to keep our troops here so we can prevent the Tories from joining up with the Royal Navy.

"I hear the navy brings along marines to fight on

the ground. They have military guns and experience in hand-to-hand fighting."

The British Royal Navy

The grand fleet of the British arrived in April 1776; they sailed away by the end of May 1776 without helping General Clinton.

Solomon said to me, "The British navy's out in the bay."

I asked, "So?"

"We have to march down to Charleston."

I was discussed, "March, march, march. Seems like a militia lives on its feet. Wish they would furnish us with some good shoes for use in the deep woods."

"Yeah. There's swamp land all about down around the ocean."

Clinton and the British attacked Charleston.

But they didn't do it together. They had difficulty joining their forces.

Solomon and I were in line abreast between the Tories and the Naval Marines. We were dug into holes and trenches shooting at anything crossing the field in front of us or heading our way.

Solomon was doing all the shooting for him and me. He'd shoot and then slide me his gun for me to load. Then he'd shoot again. He was hitting a Tory with every shot.

"Hey, Solomon, you're a great shot. I didn't realize that you could shoot so accurately."

"It's the guns. I shoot to the right of the enemy
and my gun takes my shot to the left. I hit them in
the right shoulder every time."

"Yes and we repulse them."

We fought on until it started to get dark. And about
then the British stopped a-coming.

Solomon said, "I can see the headline now. Boys
from Rich Lands save Charleston.

"Brothers Solomon and Andrew Cox drive off
British Navy."

I said, "I think we two Carolina boys are able to
work together cooperatively."

Solomon said, "A fancy way to say we do pretty
well when we're frightened."

Another Andrew Journal Entry - July 1780

The British General assigned to fight against us,
Clinton, was transferred north. We now get the fellow who was second in command, **General Cornwallis**. He's now the big honcho in charge of the
British forces in the south.

Wilmington, North Carolina, is now free of the
British forces.

During the **summer of 1778** a French fleet under
the command of **Admiral d'Estaing came to
America**.

Possible joint action with Washington was delayed when d'Estaing found it necessary, after a hurricane, to place his fleet in Boston Harbor and await repairs. In **September 1778**, he took his fleet to the Caribbean for the winter.

On **December 29, 1778**, the **British occupied Suvannah, Georgia**. We went down there to help but the British brought up Tory troops from the colony of East Florida. Soon Georgia was all in the hands of the British.

The French Go Home

In **January, 1779** d'Estaing by-passed General Washington's forces on the mainland. He sailed off for Europe and France. The French lost three war vessels to the terrible weather on the North Atlantic. Whether the admiral and his fleet would return to America was problematical.

On **February 14, 1779** - 300 Georgia and South Carolina militia routed a force of 700 Tories at **Kettle Creek**, killing 40 and capturing 75.

In 1779 the British General, Clinton, using several thousand of his New York force attacked Charleston. His force finally captured Charleston in **May**.

After taking Charleston, General Clinton returned to New York and left the further conquest of the south to his second in command, General Cornwallis.

The Battle of Camden

In **August 1780** the Patriots under General Kalb lost the Battle of Camden, South Carolina in which the Continentals fought well. Our forces escaped total disaster by headlong flight from the battle field. General Kalb was killed and General Gates took over for the Patriots. Sometimes it is good to know when to run away.

General Corwallis

More Journal Entries of Andrew Cox

1780 - General Cornwallis, prepared for his campaign against the Carolinas. He figured he needed more force so he sent Major Ferguson to Western Carolina to gather up more Tories. But the backwoodsmen of Tennessee did not appreciate having Ferguson in their midst. At Kings Mountain a swarm of militia, mostly from Tennessee defeated Ferguson and the Tories he had collected.

Cornwallis had to delay his attack on North Carolina.

The Second Battle for Wilmington

In **January, 1781** Major **James H. Craig** took Wil-

mington for the British; the major then sent detach-
ments inland to scour the countryside for Whigs
whom he captured, food which he foraged, and Tories whom he aroused to join loyalists militia units.
Cornwallis was now ready to take on North Carolina.

The Patriot army gathered to oppose him had a
few hundred regulars and an uncertain militia. The
militia included the 1st and 2nd North Carolina militia, including a half dozen Cox cousins, Jasper,
Aaron, Charles, Solomon, son of John, John and Joseph, sons of Joseph and Solomon and Andrew,
sons of Moses.

Nathaniel Green was the new commander for our
forces in the Carolinas.

Solomon was now part of the cavalry.

He rode with old Dan Morgan who was General
Green's chief lieutenant. In January, at a place called
Cowpens, they defeated the British cavalry and
slowed old Cornwallis' headlong march across the
Carolinas.

Solomon told me, "We had a much smaller force
than Cornwallis. So, while we faced his troops, we
didn't get into a major battle. We would just fall
back. We did this from South Carolina clear across
North Carolina to Virginia.

"Green then had us stop and take up a position
behind the Dan River.

"Corwallis found that he couldn't maintain his lo-
gistical support stretched so far from the sea coast.
He therefore gave up the chase and fell back to Wilmington, near the sea coast. We followed right behind him, nipping at his stragglers.

"He took his troops down through the Cox's 640 acre spread north of Rich Lands. It being fall, many of the crops were being harvested. The British promptly began reaping our wheat and collecting our cattle and milk cows. They were especially hard on our land when they found out that we had so many relatives who were fighting for the Patriots. Our Colonel Geo Mitchell of Onslow found it easy to collect volunteers to post against the British."

Andrew - 1881 - VICTORY AT YORK TOWN

General Washington on the Hudson

General Washington's army was, during the spring of 1781, on the Hudson River opposite the British in New York. Cornwallis, in the south, thinking he had nothing to fear from General Washington, moved his troops to the peninsula between the York and James Rivers. He prepared for an extensive stay awaiting more British and German troops and for the British Naval Vessels.

In late August, Washington, on the advice of his French allies, began a rapid march from the Hudson Valley to Virginia, along with about two thousand Continental troops, and four thousand French regulars.

A Patriots Victory at Elizabethtown

On August 28 - 29, 1781, 150 **Bladen County** men

won a victory at **Elizabethtown** and broke the Tory power in Bladen County. Bladen is the county on the east side of the Cape Fear River..

Thus, in the south, as of September 1781, the British controlled only Wilmington on the Cape Fear River and Charleston.

The French Fleet On Chesapeake Bay

On August 30, 1781, the French fleet under De Grasse anchored within Chesapeake Bay cutting off Cornwallis's escape route to the sea.

A week later the British fleet under Admiral Graves arrived. But after a short engagement the British had to withdraw. So the French fleet kept their station, hemming in the British army by sea at York Town, as the allied armies closed down the peninsula from the north.

The French and the Americans set up a siege in the last days of September.

On October 19, after a siege of three weeks, General Cornwallis surrendered his whole command.

Two days later Admiral Graves and his fleet reappeared; this time with General Clinton and reinforcements from New York. But General Clinton was too late to prevent a great victory for the Americans and the French. The British turned about and sailed back to New York.

General Rutherford

October, 1781 - The patriot, General Rutherford, collected enough men to march to the relief of Wilmington.

Andrew Cox said, "In November, 1781, we besieged Craig and the British at Wilmington."

After York Town

17 November, 1781 - Light-Horse Harry Lee arrived at Rutherford's camp at Wilmington with the news of Cornwallis's surrender at York Town. When this was announced to the troops, we all responded with a great cheer and many hoorays. We leaked word of the surrender to the British Commander.

18 November, 1781 - General Craig and the British troops at Wilmington mounted into ships and departed for England. .

After that...Wilmington was in quiet possession of the Patriots. We militiamen and minute men returned to our family land grants and finished harvesting late crops and preparing land for the spring planting.

The weather is turning chilly now and the leaves have all but dropped from all the hardwood trees. The squirrels are scampering about locating nuts for the oncoming Christmas season.

The Puritans long ago had a big feast to give thanks for their ability to survive in New England.

Now we give thanks for having had such great allies as the French and for being able to defeat the English at Yorktown.

BOOK FOUR - POST REVOLUTION

TWENTY SIX

BECOMING AMERICANS

Journal Entry by Hardy Cox

My name is Hardy Cox and I was born during the
height of the war just after the Declaration of Independence was published and signed by the great men
of our time. My father, Aaron Cox, was a substan-
tial North Carolina citizen. He had over 640 acres of
land, about ten children, and a Gristmill by a river.

During the war I was juggled all over the land-
scape as my parents moved about avoiding the British. My father left me, my siblings, and my mother
back in the deep woods with the fierce wild animals
of the Piedmont, while he went off to war as a min-
uteman and member of the local anti-British militia.

The young men of the day were filled with a spirited go-go adventure in which they could participate

with a full measure of life.

Only those who are young enough for war, and old enough to be trusted with a gun, can appreciate why the youth of a nation yearn for a war in which they can venture, or a nation for which they can die.

When you are born in war time you often never fully live except while a child. And then you are too young to carry the memories with you for very long.

My son, William, asked me about the Revolutionary War, "What do you remember about the **Revolutionary War?**"

I told him, "Practically nothing."

"But you must remember something."

"I was born in 1848 so I was only seventeen when the war ended. I was but a child. We were frequently on the move although we often returned to our own farm where nothing was kept up, right here near Richlands.

"My mother, Mary, had to start the farm all over again every time the British visited us. They crashed everything including the furniture, the feather beds, the stoves and fire places, our cach of stored vegetibles, our gardens, our barns, etc. She told me that my father, Aaron, would show up every once in a while to help out.

"He had to be careful to avoid being caught by the British looking for Tories or Whigs. Sometimes the British would shoot our boys on sight if they suspected them of being against the British."

"Were there Indians?"

Hardy said, "Oh sure, but not so many."

"Tories?"

"I couldn't tell. Tories and rebels looked alike.

But I most just assumed that all white men were Tories and avoided them."

"Were there British soldiers about?"

"Some. My mother, Mary, who was a daughter of (or sister to) Hardy Gregory, told me about going into town to attend dances with British officers during the periods when the British controlled most of North Carolina."

"Were you named after Hardy Gregory?"

"I think I was. He was always very kind to me."

William asked Grandmother Mary Cox (Aaron's wife) "But grandmother, didn't you fight the British?"

"Sure Billy. Mosy of the time...But sometimes we had no soldier boys left to fight here. They were off fighting the enemy with General Green or General Washington. We young women just got along as best we could."

"Was there sex?"

Grandmother Mary said, "Not with me, there wasn't. But some of the girls ended up marrying some of the British boy soldiers. After the war some of the British soldiers took their discharges in the colonies and live here now with their wives from long ago. Some of your buddies now were conceived in the period of 1778 to 1883, just after the war, by Colonial girls and British soldiers."

William asked me, "Did you get to go to school?"

"It was hard to do during wartime. But school wasn't much anyway, mostly how to farm, how to keep from being cheated when trading a cow, how to plow, how to care for a horse or cow, how to sew, how to cook over an open fireplace, how to rock babies. how to make cloth and how to please a husband or a wife."

Breaking Up the Army

"What happened to the soldiers?" William asked.
Hardy said, "Most of them were just militia so they went home and started managing their family farms.

"After the Battle of Yorktown in late 1781 most of the soldiers that could, at long last, returned to their home colonies and their families. Of course many were wounded and unable to care for themselves. Many had died for the cause. But so too, many remained members of their local militia or of the army."

"Why did they stay in the militia?"

"Mostly because they were fearful that the British would return. But also there were still some Indians about and some Tories, as well as many ruffians.

"The militia also protected the widows and orphans after the war."

From the Records

William asked, "Who were some of the returnees besides our immediate cousins?"

Hardy said, "Jesse Ballard of South Carolina was one. In 1778 he sold land on New River. This land had been granted to a Ballard in 1765. Rebecca Ballard married Francis Shackleford in 1765 and their record is recorded in a family bible. Their oldest son,

Willoughby Shackleford, sired Mary Ann Wilder who eventually married me and we had you, William, as our first son. And you were named after you grandmothers father, William Starkey."

"Any others?" William asked.

Hardy answered, "Arthur Barranau had purchased an interest in my grandfather Charles Cox's gristmill before the war. In 1779 he sold his half of the gristmill to John Jarman (who was a Cox in-law by now). The mill crossed the Little River branch of New River. John Boston (another son-in-law) and Charles Cox (son of Aaron) tests.

"More?"

Dobbs County

Hardy said, "Before the war was over, there was a 1780 tax roll. My Grand Uncle Moses and his sons, my cousins, Moses and Andrew, were still on the Dobbs County tax roll for the British."

"The British?" William asked

Hardy said, "The British were still our rulers."

William said,"Oh. How about Cousin John?"

"He was a taxpayer in Dobbs County in 1780."

"He pay the taxes to the British?"

"I don't know. But probably."

"How about the 1790 census?"

Hardy said, " Yes, census for John Cox, Dobbs (136) 20100, two males and one female; also Jesse Cox."

Duplin County (northeastern half of New Hanover on Cape Fear River).

William Cox asked me, "What of Joseph Cox?"

Hardy said, "He was on the 1783 tax roll for Duplin County. This land was originally patented by Joseph Cox along the Cape Fear River, New Hanover County. Had to pay taxes to Duplin County after 1780 when the northern part of the county changed its name to Duplin.

"Joseph's (b. 1720) family consisted of wife, Hannah, sons John and Joseph Jr.(b. c1737) and daughters, Hannah, Martha and Ketura. Also grandson, Joseph III. Mostly he lived in Charleston.

"All of Joseph's family survived the war."

Onslow County

William asked, "Any non first cousins in Onslow County about this time?"

Hardy answered, "In 1795 Jonathon Wilder and his daughter, Mary Ann (Wilder) Shackleford sold 100 acres on Back Swamp at Ready Creek Branch. Test Willoughby Shackleford (his son-in-law).

Revolutionary War Bounty Land Grants

Cox, Edward. 1784 - land grant war bounty, N.C.
640 acres to John Cox, heir.

Cox, William, war land grant, N.C. 228 acres.

Cox, Charles, N.C. pvt 1786, 640 acres
   Maybe his heirs took these grants in Geo.

Cox, Ed. N.C. pvt 1797, 640 acres to heirs.

Cox, Geo. N.C. pvt 1797, 640 acres to heirs

Cox, Jesse N.C. pvt 1797, 274 acres

Cox, Joseph N.C. pvt 1804, 640 acres to heirs

Cox, Wm. N.C. pvt 1813, 640 acres to heirs

Politics

1787 - The new Constitution was adopted.

1787 - France and England were still at war.

1788 - Presidential election. Geo. Washington was
   elected to became our first president.

1789 - Washington took office as President of the
   United States and was sworn in early in the year.

1796 - John Adams president (1797-1800).

1800 - Thomas Jefferson president (1801-1808).

1808 - James Madison president (1809-1816).

1812 - 1815 - Great Britain and America at war.

to 1815 - Napoleon Bonapart in control of France until England's victory in 1815.

1816 - James Monroe president (1817-1824).

1824 - John Quincy Adams president (1825-1828).

1828 - Andrew Jackson, president (1829-1836).

TWENTY SEVEN

1810 / 1820 CENSUS

Hardy and son, William

Son William and I (Hardy) continued our conversation about the Cox generations after Charles b. 1709, John 11, Anthony 13, Moses 17, and Joseph 1720. These initial migrants to North Carolina were all born in about the period from 1709 to 1720. They constitute the first generation of Coxes in Onslow and the surrounding counties of North Carolina.

Hardy said, "William, the children of these boys were those who were born such as to be of age to go off to the American Revolution in 1776-81. They won freedom for our United States and then they came home to the land initially patented by their fathers. I call them the second generation of Carolinian Coxes.

"The second generation were born on the mainland. They are all mentioned in earlier chapters on each first generation boy. They were born in the years beginning with 1735 to 1750.

"Who are next?" William prodded.

Hardy answered, "Next are the third generation of Coxes. These are the children of the second generation. The third generation of Coxes in North Carolina were born between the years 1760 to 1780, just too late to have been in the revolution.

We are most concerned with the children of two of Charles' (b. c1709) sons, Aaron and Charles; to a lesser degree with the children of Moses, Joseph and Anthony."

Hardy Cox

William asked, "Are you of the third generation?"

"Yes, I was born to Aaron Cox and my mother Mary Gregory Cox in 1777. They were the most productive family as will be detailed in this cha[ter. I lived at home on Grandfather Charles Cox's land near the area called Richlands. I married the widow, Priscilla (Starkey) Sweatman on January 16, 1797.

Priscilla seems to have been the daughter of William Starkey, granddaughter of Peter Starkey.

"Children?"

Not yet. First I needed a permanent house, a home for Priscilla and me. In 1800 Lawrence Jarman (Cox in-law) sold me 150 acres on Cox's Branch at a line between Aaron Cox and Lawrence Jarman, at the mouth of little Tarkiln Branch.

In 1801 my father, Aaron, sold me 80 acres for 70 pounds, part of a larger tract of 640 acres on Jethro

Marshburn's Spring Branch to Ben Marshburn's line.

In 1802 I sold 75 acres to John Cox (brother) on Cox's Branch at Hardy, John and Thomas Jarman's lines.

In 1803 Jonathon Wilder (son of Hopkins) sold Willoughby Shackleford land at Hopkins Wilder's line. [Ed. This is where Mary Ann was living for the 1810 census.]

"Did you have any more land transactions?"

Yes. In 1804 I sold 75 acres on E. side of John Cox's Branch to Thomas Jarman. This land abutted Aaron and John's land.

"Where did this land come from?"

The tract was one half of what I bought from Lawrence Jarman, an 1800 transaction.

William asked, "Any more sales?"

"In 1804 John Cox sold land to Thomas Jarman.

"In 1807 John Cox sold 75 acres on Cox's Branch to John Jarman Sr. Milly Cox, John's wife, released her dower rights."

The 1810 Census-

William asked, "What of the 1810 census?"

Hardy answered, "By 1810 this third generation of Coxes was dominating the Onslow census. I was in the Onslow census next to my sister, Hannah. Mary and Aaron Cox Jr. were close to me. You were on my census line (fourth generation) but only as a slash."

The 1810 Onslow, N. C. census was as follows:

Hardy Cox 11010 - 20100 - 3, a male 26 - 45 and female 16 - 26 with two young daughters, a boy 10 to 16, (you) and one younger boy. Neighbors included:

Geo. White and nine children.

Gaines Rowe and four children.

Mary Ann (Wilder) Shackleford, widow and four children (including Sarah).

Williams Cox (son of Moses Jr. who was son of Charles Sr.) and eight children, married to Mary Nixon.

Jonathan Wilder, widower, (Mary Ann's father) and three children.

John Shackleford and five children (two families ?) Jacky Shackleford and no children yet.

Lott Ballard and four children.

Eli Cox Jr., son of Charles Jr. and wife, (b. c1774)

Charles Cox IV - 104 - (b. c1766), son of Aaron Cox Sr. and four children.

Aaron Cox Jr. - 104 - (same age bracket as Hardy) and three young children - 20010 - 10100.

William Cox (fourth generation)

William told Hardy, "In 1816 I deeded to Eli Cox (son of Aaron) my rights in your land my rights in Mary's rights in Aaron's land without payment of any kind.

"At this time I married Sarah (Sallie) Shackleford, daughter of Willoughby Shackleford. Willoughby was the oldest son of Francis Shackleford (b.1739) and Rebecca Ballard. His wife, Mary Ann (Wilder) Shackleford, was the daughter of Jonathon Wilder. These folks all lived up and down the Cox's Branch of New River from us, near by to RichLands."

1820 Census

Hardy explained, "In the 1820 census you, William, appeared as the head-of-household in the Onslow County, North Carolina, census. You appeared on the line adjacent to my line (Hardy Cox).

"I had line no. 341 coded as follows: 110010 - 21001 interpreted as...A young man (16 - 26) has left this census line (from the 1810 census), five children at home, two boys and three girls.

"Also on line 341 were you, William Cox, (16 - 26) with a wife <26 100100 - 10100. You were a young couple with two small children.

340 Eli Cox (my brother) 110010 - 30011 - 10
A couple 26 - 45, five children, ten slaves.

340 Cader Cox (another brother) <26 210100 - 30010, six children.(third generation with fourth generation children).

339 Charles Cox (3rd bro) <26 010010 - 21010 - 2

336 Jacky Shackleford >26   000010 - 00011 - 7

329 Mrs. Shackleford (widow)   101200 - 03110 - 16, eight children.

335 Jonathan Wilder >45   000001 - 00001 - 23

336 Daniel Thompson <45   000010 - 10010 - 2
wife: Mary Ann Wilder Shackleford Thompson

335 Others include: Joel Wilder
    Lott Gregory
Jesse Wilder
Marshburn, Ben and Hannah (Hardy's sister)
Lott Ballard

"I (William) was married to Sallie Shackleford, a girl approximately three years my senior. We had two children at this time, Willoughby Shackleford Cox, born 1817, and named for Sallie's deceased father and Priscilla, born 1820, and named after William's mother. The next two children were born on the trek to Florida or actually in Florida in 1824 and 1826. One was named Starkey from my mothers family and the fourth was Susan Ann after a combination from my sisters and aunts.

Sallie and I were living with or next to Hardy in the Richlands area, on land owned by Coxes.

Off to find new land

William continued, "There was a tradition in the family whereby land was given over to one or two of the heirs so that it might be held in the family, the other family members taking a bit of money and going out into the wilderness to seek land elsewhere.

"And so it was after Aaron's death. The many sons and daughters contrived to sell their land to a single heir and the others went off elsewhere. Thus by the time of the 1830 census both Hardy and I, William Cox, fell off of the North Carolina census."

To Florida and Georgia

William continued, "Following the census of 1820, a large group from Onslow County, mostly family members of War of 1812 veterans, decided to migrate to Gadsden County, Florida. The Wilder clan, including Sallie and me, seemed to be a center of one such migration." [Ed. note: The story of this migration can be found in the Popular Historical Novel, *Reflections on Life in the Deep South,* taken from the Journals of Sallie Shackleford Cox, published in 2002].

TWENTY EIGHT

QUINCY, FLORIDA

A John Hardy Cox Journal Entry

I, John Hardy Cox, was born in 1848, one of the first sons of Willoughby S. (Shackleford) Cox, the first son of William and Sallie Cox, born in 1817 in North Carolina. My father, Willoughby, was raised as a pioneer child in the wilderness of northern Florida in the area near where the town of Quincy now exists.

I remember my childhood filled with uncles and aunts, brothers, sisters and cousins all living on our farm or nearby. We lived well on our various lands patented from the state. There were lots of Coxes and extended family members such as the Wilders who had accompanied my grandparents to Florida in the 1820's. They were on adjacent farms and plantations and in the town of Quincy. I remember the dirt yards, the bare feet and the lack of schooling.

My father had a big brood of children and two

houses, one in town where we in winter and another at our farm. We all worked the farm, much in the ways that our forebears had.

The industrial revolution was just about ready to make a run for it, actually already getting started in the northern parts of the country.

There were many negro slaves in Florida at the time, they having come over from the original states from which the white pioneers had migrated. Our wagon train in 1824 included, I was told, many negro slaves owned by the Gregory family, maybe 50 or more. Several of my great-grandaunts had married into that family and they, here in Florida, lived on one big piece of property, a plantation, which the slaves operated what amounted to a small city. There were many craftsmen and seamstresses, but it was a cotton plantation rather than tobacco.

My father, Willoughby Shackleford, like his father before him, was a craftsman carpenter and builder of houses. And like so many craftsmen he performed tasks for everyone else but neglected our own home.

By the time I was eight years old, my father and his brothers were all talking about a possible war with the Yankees from up-north. My brothers and cousins and I began playing war games, shooting up the Yankees and winning a war with them in jig time.

Then in 1860 a presidential election was held and Mr. Abraham Lincoln was elected president.

My mother, Nancy (Wilcox), told me, "Don't worry Johnny. We've had lots of new presidents before and nothing bad came of it."

My uncles were now playing war like me and my brothers. They joined the local militia and marched about, all proud with our hunting guns.

Some of the local boys my uncles ages joined active duty units and they waited for a chance to fight the Yankees. My two aunts married young men just a bit elder than themselves and these two young men also joined military units. And the girls joined auxilary units to support the boys when they got called up.

And then suddenly all the young men were gone. Mostly they went mostly to the east; eventually to join General Robert E. Lee in Virginia where about half of them were wounded and two were killed in action (KIA).

My brothers and I, and my cousins about my age, all tried to join the military too. But the new soldiers would not take me because I was still too young. But some of us got into the fight anyway. We went off and joined home guard units or arranged to serve in place of a relative for a limited unit of time.

My dad, Willoughby Shackleford Cox, was too old, being 44 in 1861. He stayed home working the farm, caring for the cattle and watching out for the women against marauding Yankees, evil roughs, and against the Black slaves who were no longer controlled by masters. Finally my father went off on campaigns in Florida, getting shot when trying to protect Marimin County to our west.

Grandpa Billy Cox, who brought our family here from North Carolina 35 years earlier also took up arms and defended our homes and families. He lasted out the war, not being wounded until 1865, dying at home in 1866 at the age of 68.

After the war my father and I took up where we had left off before the war started. But now we had to arrange to care for my grandmother Sallie and my two blood aunts and their children.

My three wounded uncles required help on their farms. For several years I rode back and forth between their farms, helping out as best I could so they didn't lose the farms to taxes or other creditors.

Across the years from 1870 to 1900, I had four wives of my own and perhaps a dozen children, many of whom died while still in childhood.

My last wife, Florrie, married me in about 1890 and bore me several children including the youngest, Monta Olen Cox, born in 1904. Monta lived much the life I had lived as a small boy, and like me, went off to assist in a war when he was just fifteen years old (in 1918).

He finished his three year hitch in 1921 in Detroit where he had met an Irish girl, Grace Murphy. He took his discharge there, married the girl, and found a job with Ford Motor Company. He went to Ford's machining apprentice and engineering schools and worked for ten years for Ford at their plants in the Dearborn, Michigan complex.

THE JADE DEPTHS OF HER EYES

From the popular historical novel by Lobo Blanco
titled,
A Dangerous Sky 030

Sagan had first met Sally Ryan on January 8, 1944
when the Battling Armadillos' P-38 pilots accomplished a midnight requisition (stealth) of over a
hundred P-38's from a remote air strip in Southwest-
ern England, flying them back to Sardinia and Fog-
gia.

Sally Ryan was a ferry pilot flying for the U.S. Air
Corps, delivering war planes from factory aprons in
the States to the far flung parts of the world.

Coming in at Dartmoor in Devon, Sally noticed a
lot of activity. As she eased the spanking new P-38
over the final fence and touched the main landing
wheels to the runway, she was unnerved by another
plane crossing the runway. It was too late for her to
hit the coal and go around. She touched the right
rudder and directed the fighter plane behind the
path being taken by the crazy occupant of the other
aircraft.

Off the runway her P-38 sped, onto the grass, over the knolls and into the saplings, now devoid of leaf or bud. The plane stopped. Sally unhooked the safety harnesses and removed her helmet revealing a very pretty face accompanied by short-clipped golden blond hair. She shook her head and ran her free hand through her hair which swirled about her, then settled back in place.

The meat wagon raced out to the plane which had gone off the runway and into the bush. Sergeant Dennis York and Corporal Chuck McAuliffe sprang from the vehicle and raced into the bush to the plane.

There was no fire. The hatch was open and the pilot was extracting himself from the gondola where the cockpit was located in a P-38. But the pilot was no "him". It was a "her".

"I'll be damned," Sergeant York said.

"I'll second that," said McAuliffe.

The corpsmen pulled on the ladder lever, then climbed the ladder to the wingroot, moving swiftly up to where Sally Ryan sat in the gondola.

"Switches off?" asked Chuck, the first up.

"Some arrival, 'eh?" Sally said, swinging her head. Then she said, "Who the hell was that scarecrow crossing the runway when I touched down?"

Sergeant York said, "Let's get away from here fast. The plane may yet catch fire or explode. This is no place for a social conversation."

"Good point," Sally said. "Here's my bag." She tossed down a duffle bag which she'd carried behind the seat of the fighter.

"I'll bring your parachute," said Chuck.

Quickly the three Americans moved away from the plane. As the three slipped off the trailing edge of the wings and cleared the bush back, two more jeeps came racing up. The Engineeering Officer jumped from one and a Captain and Second Lieutenant, both pilots came from the second.

Sally examined the three. "Who was the dumb head who was driving a plane across the runway when I was trying to land?"

"Not me," said the Engineer. "I've got to get this plane repaired and out of here by tomorrow. What's wrong with it?"

"Nothing. It is or was in great condition before I had to go thrashing about the countryside avoiding dumn throttle jockies."

The Engineering Officer moved on into the bush to examine the airplane and to determine what had to be done to extract it from the field of small trees.

"I'm the guilty party mam," said Jonny Sagan.

Sally walked up to the pilot and thought about bashing him across the mouth. But he looked so forlorn and contrite. She was from Texas and thought he looked like a sick cow. She found herself first putting her hands on his shoulders. Then standing on her toes she took his head by the ears and drawing his head to her, she kissed him soundly.

"My gosh, I'm in heaven," said the pilot, Sagan, completely baffled by the aviatrix's behavior. But, he noted, she was certainly a cute girl, short-blond hair and all. He looked down into her eyes. The jaded depth of them drew his lips to hers. He returned the first kiss, then circumscribed the girl's waist with his arms and gave her yet another kiss.

The pilot Ryan tried to move away but Sagan

held her closer.

Finally he said, "Wait until I tell Kelly about this. This is his character, not mine."

She asked, "What are you talking about?"

"I have a pilot friend to whom all the girls gravitate. Nobody goes around kissing me, only him."

Sally questioned, "He kisses you?"

Jonny said, "No. The girls kiss him."

Sally said, "Well, I'm glad we got that straight."

"I hope you're feeling O.K."

"I'm just thankful to be alive," Sally said, as she extracted herself from the embrace.

"I'm glad you are too," said Jonny.

Sally stepped back and looked him in the eye and smiled, "Maybe we were meant to meet."

Jonny said. "There's coffee up at Operations. How about sharing a cup?"

The two pilots, boy and girl, jumped into the waiting jeep and headed off for the Operations Office.

"That's my boy," said Captain Tom Brody, who had driven Jonny Sagan out to the accident site. He watched his jeep as Sagan drove it out of sight, leaving Brody with no transportation.

January 8, 1944
Somewhere Over France

"Paul. I forgot to set my altimeter. How high are we now?" Rex Hawkins asked. "Over."

"Angels twelve and a half. Rescue 36. Over and

ISBN 141203217-2